The Pocket Encyclopedia of World Aircraft in Color

BOMBERS IN SERVICE

PATROL AND TRANSPORT AIRCRAFT

SINCE 1960

The Pocket Encyclopedia
of World Aircraft in Color

BOMBERS IN SERVICE

PATROL AND TRANSPORT AIRCRAFT

SINCE 1960

by

KENNETH MUNSON

Illustrated by
JOHN W. WOOD

Frank Friend
Brian Hiley
William Hobson
Tony Mitchell
Jack Pelling

THE MACMILLAN COMPANY

First published in the English edition 1972
© 1972 Blandford Press Ltd.

The original volume *Bombers, Patrol and Transport Aircraft*
first published 1966
(Reprinted 1967)

First American edition 1972
Library of Congress Catalog Card Number 72–78613

THE MACMILLAN COMPANY
866 Third Avenue, New York, N.Y. 10022

Color section printed in Holland by Ysel Press Ltd.
Text printed and books bound in Great Britain by
Richard Clay (The Chaucer Press) Ltd., Bungay, Suffolk

PREFACE

When the original two volumes in this 'Pocket Encyclopaedia' were published in 1966 they were regarded as something of an experiment, and included the major aircraft types then in service, regardless of age. In the six years which have followed, the original idea has given rise to a whole series of volumes to cover the major civil as well as military aircraft of the world, from the Wright *Flyer* onwards, each volume covering a convenient period of time.

When these original two titles were due for revision, it seemed appropriate to revise them completely to cover the period from 1960 onwards, discarding earlier aircraft which would then appear in other volumes covering the period 1945–60. The effect of this has been to permit the inclusion of a greater variety of contemporary aircraft, so that some three-quarters of the present volume consists of new or extensively-revised material.

As usual, thanks are again due to Ian D. Huntley for his continuing advice on the matter of colours and markings. Friends or other sources who kindly made material available or provided help in other ways included, particularly, *AiReview* magazine, Mário Roberto vaz Carneiro, the British and US journals of the IPMS, Marcelo W. Miranda, Stephen Peltz, Profile Publications Ltd and John W. R. Taylor. To them also my thanks are extended, as well as to Doreen Hobson for kindly undertaking the typing of the manuscript.

Kenneth Munson

April 1972

5

INTRODUCTION

Broadly speaking, the aircraft described and illustrated in the companion volume on 'Fighters' are those whose duties, in operations against a hostile power, would take place within, or at a reasonably short distance from, the areas occupied by their own forces. In this volume is a further selection of warplanes, comprising those types that would be required to fly over greater distances, carrying the war back to an enemy's home ground or bringing up forces and supplies from home bases far away.

These aircraft can be separated into two basic camps, according to whether their primary function is of a strategic or a tactical nature. Webster defines a strategic role as one 'designed or trained to strike an enemy at the sources of his military, economic or political power'; and a tactical operation as one 'involving actions or means of less magnitude or at a shorter distance from a base of operations than those of strategy; of, relating to, or designed for air attack in close support of friendly ground forces'. The bombers of today can, like the fighters, be divided into a number of more specialised sub-categories, including intercontinental and medium range strategic bombers, short- and medium-range tactical bombers, night interdictors and low-level strike aircraft. Most of these normally have an internal bay for the stowage of bombs or other weapons, although the stand-off bombs carried by British, French, Russian and US strategic bombers are mounted externally or semi-externally. But a full bomb bay no longer represents necessarily the maximum capacity of most bomber aircraft. Even the giant B-52 Stratofortress, with an internal capacity of fifty-four 750 lb high-explosive bombs, has been subjected to structural reinforcement in order to carry a further quantity on pylons underneath the wings; and the FB-111A, Strategic Air Command's bomber version of the swing-wing F-111 fighter, carries this step to what may seem a ludicrous extreme by being able to carry no fewer than *forty-eight* 750 lb bombs under its wings while the actual bomb bay is occupied by only two bombs of the same modest size.

One strategic bomber, the supersonic B-58 Hustler, remained unique among serving aircraft until its retirement in 1970 in having been designed deliberately without any internal provision at all for an ordnance load. Instead it carried its total offensive load in an aerodynamic 'weapons pod' which also contained fuel for the outward half of the journey. Thus the whole pod could be released when the target was reached, leaving the Hustler 'clean' for a fast homeward run. The Hustler, incidentally, makes an interesting comparison with the Soviet Tupolev Tu-22, proving the point that aerodynamic beauty is no longer necessarily a complete guide to performance or capability. The Tu-22 is a far more attractive aeroplane aesthetically than the wasp-like, pod-bedecked Hustler, yet the US bomber not only had the better performance of the two but entered service several years ahead of the Tu-22.

Another inevitable comparison is that between the American B-52 and the Russian Tu-95. Both are comparable in terms of size, shape, weight and original purpose, and have been in service for a similar length of time. However, whereas the B-52 has turbojet engines (turbofans in the B-52H), the Tu-95 is powered by propeller-turbines. Admittedly these turboprops are no mean performers, but even so the Tu-95's top speed is still some 100 mph (160 km/hr) below that of the Stratofortress, and the choice of this form of powerplant for an intercontinental bomber caused the Russian aeroplane to be regarded with some scepticism when its existence first became known in the west. The passage of time, however, revealed the true value of the Tu-95 to the Soviet Union. This lay not so much in its intrinsic value as a warplane, but in the effect which the very existence of an intercontinental bomber in the Russian inventory had upon defence activity in the United States. For a relatively small cost – for the Tu-95 was developed in parallel with the Tu-114 commercial airliner – the USSR succeeded in causing the expenditure of many extra millions of dollars on advanced radar and electronic defence networks across the North American continent, not to mention the accelerated development of defensive aircraft and missile systems. Now that its original purpose has been achieved, the Tu-95 has been switched almost exclusively to long-range land and oversea reconnaissance and early warning work, though with the stand-off weapon that it can carry it could still presumably be called into use as a strike weapon; but it is significant that, so far as is known, no replacement aircraft of comparable unrefuelled range has been produced to take its place.

British and French strategic bombers share a fundamental design advantage in that they are considerably closer geographically to their potential target. Hence, they do not have to carry anything like the quantity of fuel needed by a B-52 or a Tu-95 to reach its objective, and are consequently a great deal smaller than these giant aeroplanes. They can, however, be refuelled in flight by tanker aircraft if required to carry out missions of greater duration. The Mirage IV-A, a scaled-up development of Dassault's delta fighter, gives the French *force de frappe* a nuclear weapon carrier with a Mach 2 performance, while Britain's dwindling force of Mk 2 Vulcans attains rather less than half this speed. There is not quite the disparity in effectiveness here that might be assumed from the relative speeds of the aircraft concerned, for the bomber, coming in very low – well under a thousand feet – at high subsonic speed has a better chance of eluding an enemy's ground-based early warning radar system until the very last minute, and is less vulnerable to anti-aircraft defences than a faster and higher-flying attacker. High speed at height is, however, useful over the early part of the flight, and both bombers are able to perform effectively at either high or low level. High speed at both low and high levels gives SAC's new FB-111A, with its advanced terrain-following radar, this ability to come in fast to a target at only 200 ft (60 m) altitude, virtually undetected by any ground-based radar. A larger and even more sophisticated swing-wing strategic bomber is the North American Rockwell B-1A, in the design development stage in the early 1970s. Late in 1971 came the first firm indications that Russia, too, has produced a swing-wing bomber. Code-named 'Backfire', it was said to have two powerful NK-144 afterburning engines, an unrefuelled radius of more than 3,000 miles (4,830 km), and to have reached flight test status.

While 1966 marked the final retirement from front-line service of the US Air Force's veteran B-47 Stratojet medium bomber, its Russian counterpart, the Tu-16, continues to soldier on with the Soviet air and naval air arms. But whereas the B-47 served no other country outside America, the Tu-16 has been supplied since 1961 to pro-Soviet key points in the Middle and Far East, the United Arab Republic and Indonesia, and those delivered to both governments are provided with Russian air-to-surface anti-shipping missiles.

Aside from the Tu-22, recent bomber development in the Soviet Union seems to have produced only one notable type (the Yakovlev Yak-28 light tactical bomber) that has yet entered service. The

Yak-28 provides, after an uncommonly long gestation period, a Soviet Air Force successor to the veteran Il-28 Beagle, although so far there is no evidence of its allocation to any of the numerous Beagle-equipped air forces outside of Russia. The Yak-28 represents an updating of the Il-28 concept rather than a particularly sophisticated replacement for it; and it is hardly in the same class as, say, the Hawker Siddeley Buccaneer.

Mention of the Buccaneer leads naturally to a consideration of the other naval bomber aircraft now in service. As Britain's only serving aeroplane in this category, and now in process of being transferred from the Royal Navy to the RAF, it has few parallels except in the US Navy. The Soviet naval air arm relies largely on land-based adaptations of standard air force types, the Tu-16 and Tu-95. The Buccaneers of South Africa's Maritime Command are also deployed from bases on land. Argentina and Australia now have the excellent Douglas Skyhawk, which will serve them at least into the mid-1970s; but otherwise the use of bombers from carrier bases is virtually the prerogative of the United States Navy, which has a variety of such types ranging in size from the tiny Skyhawk upwards. Even here, the Vigilante has now been allocated a primary reconnaissance role in lieu of its original function.

However, while the bigger, faster and more expensive bombers owe their existence mainly to the threat of war on a global scale, there is another category which has been very much to the fore in the past decade or so in the all-too-frequent border incidents, minor conflicts and wars of attrition like the one in Vietnam. The aircraft in this category, mostly American in origin, are variously classed as 'commando' or 'coin' (an abbreviation of *counter-in*surgency) types, and functionally they represent a logical development from what used to be called the police aeroplane or, in even earlier days, the colonial aeroplane. It was the Korean war of 1950–53 which laid the foundations of today's emphasis on the coin aircraft, and two piston-engined types in particular stand out in this field. The twin-engined B-26 Invader and the single-engined AD Skyraider, both Douglas types, were on the verge of being retired from active US service at this time, but because of the outbreak of hostilities were retained on the active list. Korea was the first full-scale military confrontation in which the opposing elements were equipped substantially with jet aircraft, and much has since been written and said of the air battles between the MiG-15 on the one hand and the Meteor and

Sabre on the other. This tended to overshadow the notable part played in the struggle by piston-engined aircaft, but it is a fact that, despite the arrival of more and more jet aircraft in the fighting areas, the Invader, Skyraider and others continued to be used in undiminishing numbers throughout the whole period of the war. In Algeria, the French too found that the piston engine still had advantages over the jet in certain applications, and subsequent international events have served to establish the coin aircraft as a type with a positive place in 'limited war' engagements. The Combat Applications Group of the USAF Special Air Warfare Center at Eglin Air Force Base, Florida, has given many veteran aircraft a new lease of life by modifying them for coin duties with TAC Commando Air Wings operating in Vietnam. The Skyraider, nearly twenty years after its Korean war service, is still one of the best coin aircraft in the business, despite the predominance nowadays of other carrier types such as the Skyhawk and A-6 Intruder, and by more recent types such as North American Rockwell's excellent OV-10A Bronco.

This is not the place to argue the future or otherwise of the aircraft carrier as a capital ship, but one thing that brooks no argument at all is the threat presented by the existence of the missile-carrying submarine. Such a means of attack is the most difficult to detect of any yet devised, and presents the defence organisations of both east and west with a prodigious task of surveillance, not to mention that of being able to counter such an attack if it is ever launched. The needle-in-a-haystack job of locating and keeping track of surface vessels is arduous enough, but to find and follow an unseen, underwater craft from the air is a hundred times more difficult. Any aeroplane designed for such a role must have two primary attributes: the ability to stay aloft for hours at a time on patrols far away from its home base, and the space to carry a vast array of radio, radar, echo-ranging, magnetic and electronic detection equipment. It must also carry a substantial crew to man this equipment, and allow space for their 'operations room' and sleeping quarters (and, perhaps, for a relief crew if the patrol is to be an especially long one). None matches the Super Constellation's maximum complement of thirty-one crew members, but ten or a dozen are not uncommon in aircraft of this type. The modern anti-submarine patrol aircraft combines both the 'hunter' and 'killer' roles in the one airframe, carrying an assortment of sea mines, depth charges, acoustic homing torpedoes and the like with which to attack its quarry. The aircraft in this class come in many shapes and sizes, ranging from the relatively small, single-engined Alizé through the medium-sized Grumman Tracker and Lockheed Viking to larger, land-based types such as the Neptune, Orion, Atlantic, Nimrod and Argus. The carrier-borne aircraft can afford to be smaller, of course, since they have a mobile base and do not need to cover such great distances as those operating from shore stations.

There are a growing number of types whose function is to provide airborne early warning of attack, be this from submarine, surface vessel or even land-based aircraft. These include the Mk 3 Gannet of the Fleet Air Arm and the American Tracer and Hawkeye, all distinguishable by large external radomes of various shapes and sizes. These aircraft normally carry no weapons themselves to launch any form of counter-attack, although a part of the Hawkeye's job is to remain aloft after relaying a warning to act as an aerial 'command post' directing the retaliatory force. Even larger than Hawkeye are the USSR's 'Moss' derivative of the Tu-114 and the forthcoming Boeing AWACS, based on the commercial Model 707-320.

Early warning of possible attack is by no means the only form which modern reconnaissance takes. Fundamentally, there are at least three other categories into which reconnaissance can be subdivided: these are photographic, electronics and weather reconnaissance. The nature of photographic reconnaissance needs little elaboration here: it, and the allied art of photographic interpretation, came into their own during World War 2, and techniques have advanced significantly since then, both for military applications and in the civil fields of aerial survey and map-making. Electronics reconnaissance is that branch of reconnaissance devoted to monitoring the radio and radar transmissions of potentially hostile powers, and perhaps providing appropriate electronic countermeasures (ECM), while weather reconnaissance has obvious value to the military as well as to civilian establishments.

Speed has long been one of the prime requisites of the military reconnaissance aircraft, and for this reason many present-day PR types are converted from current fighters. However, with the advances made in modern high definition camera lenses and photographic emulsions, pictures can now be taken by relatively slow-flying machines operating at altitudes beyond the reach of most intercepting fighters. Even enlargements of pictures taken at a height of 50,000 ft (15,240 m), which is not an exceptional altitude in PR terms, can, with a resolution as precise as a hundred lines to the millimetre, reveal features as tiny as a golf ball or as fine as the white lines on a tennis court. The slow-but-high approach to photographic reconnaissance gave the world the notorious Lockheed U-2, the only currently-serving military aeroplane to be designed purely for reconnaissance work; this was virtually a jet-powered sailplane, and has its Russian counterpart in the form of the Mandrake, an extended-span development of the Yak-25 fighter. Most other high altitude reconnaissance within the Earth's atmosphere is undertaken by modified versions of existing bomber aircraft, the fighter/reconnaissance types being generally more suitable for low-level work. Russia uses the Tu-16, Tu-95 and Tu-22; the United States has the Martin RB-57D and RB-57F – the latter surely the ultimate in Canberra 'stretch' – and now has, in the Mach 3 Lockheed SR-71, the world's fastest and highest-flying reconnaissance aeroplane. Improved electronic flash equipment now facilitates night photographic work; infra-red, especially when used in conjunction with colour emulsions, provides an admirable means of 'unmasking' camouflaged installations; and the sideways-looking airborne radar and terrain-mapping radar, such as that carried by the RA-5C Vigilante and the Grumman Mohawk respectively, gives excellent coverage at low levels. An interesting variation from more conventional practice is that provided by the drone-carrying DC-130A Hercules which has been used in South-east Asia. The information is gathered by remotely-controlled Ryan Firebee drones launched from beneath the wings of the Hercules, after which the drones are monitored back to land by parachute in preselected recovery areas. The Firebee and other drone vehicles will be heard of much more in the years ahead, as a whole new breed of these RPVs (remotely-piloted vehicles) is developed to carry out many of the missions at present undertaken by manned aircraft.

The Hercules, of course, versatile though it is, really belongs to the final category covered by this volume, the field of transportation. The world's battles are still fought out very largely by the man on the ground, and his very existence, as well as the maintenance of his food and equipment supplies, rely heavily on air transport backing. In the matter of shape, size or capability, transport aircraft range from small, single-engined types to such giants as the An-22, Star-Lifter and Galaxy.

Several veterans of World War 2 continue to give yeoman service.

They include – inevitably – the ageless and seemingly irreplaceable DC-3, known in military guise as the C-47, and the Fairchild C-123 Provider. Among the more modern types, the short/medium-range Caribou and Buffalo, together with transport helicopters, provide close-support transportation of and for the ground forces in the field; the ubiquitous Hercules carries many tactical loads over medium ranges; while the long-range strategic hauls are flown by the Star-Lifter and Galaxy.

The Royal Air Force has two excellent strategic transports in the VC10 trooper and the Belfast freighter, the freight and troop tactical transport roles being undertaken by the Argosy and Andover Mark 1. Other tactical transports deserving mention are the French Noratlas, which has given way to the Hercules in some quarters and the Tran-sall C-160 in others; and Russia's An-12, developed from civil pas-senger airliners of similar pattern. France's Noratlases were for many years backed by a small force of the portly Sahara; Canada has only recently retired the Yukon, a development of the Argus ASW aircraft which in turn was derived from the Britannia airliner. A more recent concept is the COD (Carrier-On-board Delivery) transport for the provisioning of US Navy carriers at sea. This need has been met by adaptations of first the Grumman Tracker and later the Hawkeye, with enlarged fuselages for carrying cargo.

There are no vertical take-off transports yet in service, although some interesting designs are undergoing evaluation, but much design ingenuity has been exercised in shortening the take-off and landing demands of more conventional transport airframes; the Caribou and Buffalo are two excellent STOL transports which have already proved their worth in the Vietnamese operations, and France has produced the Breguet 941S. Military aircraft may be becoming more complex and more specialised, but at the same time they are also becoming very much more flexible, to meet the ever-changing demands of modern operational conditions.

THE COLOUR PLATES

As an aid to identification, the eighty pages of colour plates which follow have been arranged in a basically visual order, with propeller-driven aircraft first, followed by jet aircraft. The reference number of each aircraft corresponds to the appropriate text matter. An index to all types appears on pages 153 to 155.

The 'split' plan view, adopted to give both upper and lower surface markings within a single plan outline, depicts the colour scheme appearing above and below either the port or starboard half of the aircraft, according to whichever aspect is shown in the side elevation.

1

Antonov An-2P of the DOSAAF, *ca* 1961-62. *Engine:* One 1,000 h.p. Shvetsov ASh-62IR nine-cylinder radial. *Span:* 59 ft. 8½ in. (18.18 m.). *Length.* 41 ft. 10 in. (12.75 m.). *Wing area:* 769.9 sq. ft. (71.53 sq.m.). *Normal take-off weight:* 12,125 lb. (5,500 kg.). *Maximum speed:* 157 m.p.h. (253 km/hr.) at 5,750 ft. (1,750 m.). *Service ceiling:* 14,275 ft. (4,350 m.). *Range:* 560 miles (905 km.).

REGENTE (Brazil)

2
Neiva L-42 Regente of the Fôrça Aérea Brasileira, 1970. *Engine:* One 180 h.p.
Lycoming O-360-A1D four-cylinder horizontally-opposed type. *Span:* 29 ft. 11½ in.
(9.13 m.). *Length:* 23 ft. 1 in. (7.04 m.). *Wing area:* 144.8 sq. ft. (13.45 sq. m.).
Maximum take-off weight: 2,293 lb. (1,040 kg.). *Maximum cruising speed:* 156
m.p.h. (252 km/hr.) at sea level. *Service ceiling:* 12,000 ft. (3,660 m.). *Maximum
range:* 590 miles (950 km.).

COURIER (U.S.A.)

3

Helio U-10A Super Courier of the USAF, *ca* 1965. *Engine:* One 295 h.p. Lycoming GO-480-G1D6 six-cylinder horizontally-opposed type. *Span:* 39 ft. 0 in. (11.89 m.). *Length:* 31 ft. 0 in. (9.45 m.). *Wing area:* 231.0 sq. ft. (21.46 sq. m.). *Maximum take-off weight:* 3,850 lb. (1,746 kg.). *Maximum speed:* 167 m.p.h. (269 km/hr.) at sea level. *Service ceiling:* 20,500 ft. (6,250 m.). *Range:* 615 miles (990 km.).

LOCKHEED YO-3A (U.S.A.)

4
Lockheed YO-3A prototype in US Army markings, 1969. *Engine:* One modified 210 h.p. Continental six-cylinder horizontally-opposed type. *Span:* 57 ft. 0 in. (17.37 m.). *Length:* 30 ft. 0 in. (9.14 m.). *Wing area:* approx 180.0 sq. ft. (16.70 sq. m.). *Weight and performance data classified.*

5
Douglas A-1H Skyraider of the Vietnamese Air Force. 1965. *Engine:* One 2,700 h.p. Wright R-3350-26WA eighteen-cylinder radial. *Span:* 50 ft. 0 in. (15.24 m.). *Length:* 39 ft. 2½ in. (11.95 m.). *Wing area:* 400.0 sq. ft. (37.16 sq. m.). *Maximum take-off weight:* 25,000 lb. (11,340 kg.). *Maximum speed:* 285 m.p.h. (459 km/hr.) at 18,500 ft. (5,640 m.). *Service ceiling:* 28,500 ft. (8,685 m.). *Radius on internal fuel:* 1,145 miles (1,840 km.).

ALIZÉ (France)

6

Breguet 1050 Alizé of the Aéronavale, ca 1964. *Engine:* One 2,100 e.s.h.p. Rolls-Royce Dart RDa.21 turboprop. *Span:* 51 ft. 2¼ in. (15.60 m.). *Length:* 45 ft. 6 in. (13.87 m.). *Wing area:* 387.5 sq. ft. (36.00 sq. m.). *Normal take-off weight:* 18,100 lb. (8,210 kg.). *Maximum speed:* 282 m.p.h. (454 km/hr.) at 10,000 ft. (3,050 m.). *Maximum range:* 1,324 miles (2,130 km.).

GANNET (U.K.)

7

Westland (Fairey) Gannet AEW.Mk 3 of No. 849 Squadron Royal Navy, on detachment on board HMS *Ark Royal, ca* 1961. *Engine:* One 3,875 e.h.p. Bristol Siddeley Double Mamba 102 turboprop. *Span:* 54 ft. 7 in. (16.64 m.); *folded,* 20 ft. 0 in. (6.10 m.). *Length:* 43 ft. 11 in. (13.39 m.). *Wing area:* 490.0 sq. ft. (45.52 sq. m.). *Maximum take-off weight:* approx. 24,000 lb. (10,886 kg.). *Maximum speed:* 250 m.p.h. (402 km/hr.) at 5,000 ft. (1,525 m.). *Service ceiling:* 25,000 ft. (7,620 m.). *Range with underwing fuel tanks:* approx. 800 miles (1,285 km.).

CESSNA O-2 (U.S.A.)

8

Cessna O-2A (Forward Air Controller's aircraft) of the USAF, 1968-69. *Engines:* Two 210 h.p. Continental IO-360-C six-cylinder horizontally-opposed type. *Span:* 38 ft. 2 in. (11.63 m.). *Length:* 29 ft. 9 in. (9.07 m.). *Wing area:* 202.5 sq. ft. (18.81 sq. m.). *Take-off weight:* 4,300 lb. (1,950 kg.). *Maximum speed:* 199 m.p.h. (320 km/hr.) at sea level. *Service ceiling:* 18,000 ft. (5,490 m.). *Maximum range, standard fuel:* 755 miles (1,215 km.).

9
Britten-Norman BN-2A Islander of the Abu Dhabi Defence Force, early 1968.
Engines: Two 260 h.p. Lycoming O-540-E4C5 six-cylinder horizontally-opposed
type. *Span:* 49 ft. 0 in. (14.94 m.). *Length:* 35 ft. 7¾ in. (10.86 m.). *Wing area:* 325.0
sq. ft. (30.19 sq. m.). *Maximum take-off weight:* 6,300 lb. (2,857 kg.). *Maximum
speed:* 170 m.p.h. (273 km/hr.) at sea level. *Service ceiling:* 14,600 ft. (4,450 m.).
Maximum range: 870 miles (1,400 km.).

PIAGGIO P166M (Italy)

10

Piaggio P166M of the Aeronautica Militare Italiano, *ca* 1962. *Engines:* Two 340 h.p. Lycoming GSO-480-B1C6 six-cylinder horizontally-opposed type. *Span:* 46 ft. 9 in. (14.25 m.). *Length:* 38 ft. 0¾ in. (11.60 m.). *Wing area:* 285.9 sq. ft. (26.56 sq. m.). *Maximum take-off weight:* 8,113 lb. (3,680 kg.). *Maximum speed:* 223 m.p.h. (359 km/hr.). *Service ceiling:* 25,500 ft. (7.770 m.). *Maximum range:* 1.290 miles (2 080 km.).

MITSUBISHI MU-2 (Japan)

11

Mitsubishi MU-2E (MU-2S) of the Japan Air Self Defence Force, 1969. *Engines:* Two 605 e.s.h.p. AiResearch TPE 331-25A/25B turboprops. *Span:* 39 ft. 2½ in. (11.95 m.). *Length:* 35 ft. 1¼ in. (10.70 m.). *Wing area:* 178.1 sq. ft. (16.55 sq. m.). *Maximum take-off weight:* 10,053 lb. (4,560 kg.). *Maximum cruising speed:* 310 m.p.h. (500 km/hr.) at 10,000 ft. (3,050 m.). *Service ceiling:* 25,925 ft. (7,900 m.). *Maximum range:* 1,550 miles (2,495 km.).

BASSET (U.K.)

12

Beagle Basset CC.Mk 1 of Southern Communications Squadron RAF, 1968.
Engines: Two 310 h.p. Rolls-Royce/Continental GIO-470-A six-cylinder horizontally-opposed type. *Span:* 45 ft. 9½ in. (13.96 m.). *Length:* 33 ft. 3 in. (10.13 m.).
Wing area: 214.0 sq. ft. (19.90 sq. m.). *Maximum take off weight:* 7,500 lb.
(3,402 kg.). *Maximum cruising speed:* 207 m.p.h. (333 km/hr.) at 10,000 ft.
(3,050 m.). *Service ceiling:* 17,500 ft. (5,330 m.). *Range with payload of 950 lb.
(431 kg.):* 1,175 miles (1,890 km.)

BEECHCRAFT U-21 (U.S.A.)

13

Beechcraft RU-21D of the US Army, 1970. *Engines:* Two 550 s.h.p. Pratt & Whitney (UACL) PT6A-20 turboprops. *Span:* 45 ft. 10½ in. (13.98 m.). *Length:* 35 ft. 6 in. (10.82 m.). *Wing area:* 279.7 sq. ft. (25.98 sq. m.). *Maximum take-off weight:* 9,650 lb. (4,377 kg). *Maximum cruising speed:* 245 m.p.h. (395 km/hr.) at 10,000 ft. (3,050 m.). *Service ceiling:* 25,500 ft. (7,775 m.). *Typical range:* 1,167 miles (1,878 km.).

AZOR (Spain)

14

CASA 207-A (T.7A) Azor of the Ejército del Aire, *ca* 1961. *Engines:* Two 2,040 h.p. Bristol Hercules 730 fourteen-cylinder radials. *Span:* 91 ft. 2½ in. (27.80 m.). *Length:* 68 ft. 5 in. (20.85 m.). *Wing area:* 923.2 sq. ft. (85.80 sq. m.). *Maximum take-off weight:* 36,375 lb. (16,500 kg.). *Maximum cruising speed:* 249 m.p.h. (400 km/hr.) at 12,340 ft. (3,760 m.). *Service ceiling:* 26,250 ft. (8,000 m.). *Range with 30 passengers:* 1,620 miles (2,610 km.).

SKYTRAIN (U.S.A.)

15

Douglas C-47A Skytrain of Eskadrille 721, Royal Danish Flyvevåbnet, *ca* 1964.
Engines: Two 1,200 h.p. Pratt & Whitney R-1830-90C Twin Wasp fourteen-cylinder
radials. *Span:* 95 ft. 0 in. (28.96 m.). *Length:* 64 ft. 5½ in. (19.65 m.). *Wing area:*
987.0 sq. ft. (91.70 sq. m.). *Normal take-off weight:* 26,000 lb. (11,793 kg.).
Maximum speed: 229 m.p.h. (368 km/hr.) at 7,500 ft. (2,285 m.). *Service ceiling:*
24,000 ft. (7,315 m.). *Normal range:* 1,500 miles (2,415 km.).

TROOPSHIP (Netherlands)

16

Fokker-VFW F.27 Mk 400M Troopship of the Sudan Air Force, 1966. *Engines:* Two 2,050 s.h.p. plus 525 lb. (238 kg.) st Rolls-Royce Dart RDa.7 Mk 532-7 turboprops. *Span:* 95 ft. 2 in. (29.00 m.). *Length:* 77 ft. 3½ in. (23.56 m.). *Wing area:* 753.5 sq. ft. (70.00 sq. m.). *Maximum take-off weight:* 43,500 lb. (19,730 kg.). *Cruising speed:* 295 m.p.h. (474 km/hr.). at 20,000 ft. (6,100 m.). *Service ceiling:* 29,500 ft. (8,990 m.). *Operational radius:* 620 miles (1,000 km.).

HERALD (U.K.)

17

Handley Page Herald Srs. 401 of the Royal Malaysian Air Force, *ca* 1965. *Engines:* Two 2,105 e.h.p. Rolls-Royce Dart RDa.7 Mk 527 turboprops. *Span:* 94 ft. 9 in. (28.88 m.). *Length:* 75 ft. 6 in. (23.01 m.). *Wing area:* 886.0 sq. ft. (82.31 sq. m.). *Maximum take-off weight:* 43,000 lb. (19,500 kg.). *Maximum cruising speed:* 275 m.p.h. (443 km/hr.) at 15,000 ft. (4,575 m.) *Service ceiling:* 27,900 ft. (8,500 m.). *Range with maximum payload of 11,242 lb. (5,100 kg):* 700 miles (1,125 km.).

33

GII (Argentina)

18

FMA IA 50 GII of the I Brigada Aérea, Fuerza Aérea Argentina, 1968. *Engines:* Two 930 s.h.p. Turboméca Bastan VI-A turboprops. *Span:* 64 ft. 3¼ in. (19.59 m.) without tip-tanks. *Length:* 50 ft. 2½ in. (15.30 m.). *Wing area:* 450.0 sq. ft. (41.81 sq. m.). *Maximum take-off weight:* 16,204 lb. (7,350 kg.). *Maximum cruising speed:* 305 m.p.h. (491 km/hr.). *Service ceiling:* 41,000 ft. (12,500 m.). *Range with maximum payload of 3,307 lb. (1,500 kg.):* 1,240 miles (1,995 km.).

BANDEIRANTE (Brazil)

19

EMBRAER EMB-110 Bandeirante in the insignia of the Fôrça Aérea Brasileira. *Engines:* Two 680 s.h.p. Pratt & Whitney (UACL) PT6A-27 turboprops. *Span:* 50 ft. 3¼ in. (15.32 m.). *Length:* 46 ft. 8¼ in. (14.23 m.). *Wing area:* 312.2 sq. ft. (29.00 sq. m.). *Maximum take-off weight:* 11,244 lb. (5,100 kg.). *Maximum cruising speed:* 260 m.p.h. (418 km/hr.) at 9,840 ft. (3,000 m.). *Service ceiling:* 27,950 ft. (8,520 m.). *Maximum range:* 1,150 miles (1,850 km.).

CARIBOU (Canada)

20

de Havilland Canada DHC-4 Caribou of the Kuwait Air Force, *ca* 1966. *Engines:* Two 1,450 h.p. Pratt & Whitney R-2000-7M2 fourteen-cylinder radials. *Span:* 95 ft. 7½ in. (29.15 m.). *Length:* 72 ft. 7 in. (22.13 m.). *Wing area:* 912.0 sq. ft. (84.72 sq. m.). *Normal maximum take-off weight:* 28,500 lb. (12,928 kg.). *Maximum cruising speed:* 182 m.p.h. (293 km/hr.). at 7,500 ft. (2,285 m.). *Service ceiling:* 24,800 ft. (7,560 m.). *Range with maximum payload of 8,740 lb. (3,965 kg.):* 242 miles (390 km.).

BUFFALO (Canada)

21

de Havilland Canada DHC-5 (C-8A) Buffalo of the US Army, *ca* 1965. *Engines:* Two 2,850 e.s.h.p. General Electric T64-GE-10 turboprops. *Span:* 96 ft. 0 in. (29.26 m.). *Length:* 77 ft. 4 in. (23.57 m.). *Wing area:* 945.0 sq. ft. (87.80 sq. m.). *Maximum take-off weight:* 41,000 lb. (18,598 kg.). *Maximum cruising speed:* 271 m.p.h. (435 km/hr.) at 10,000 ft. (3,050 m.). *Service ceiling:* 30,000 ft. (9,150 m.). *Range with maximum payload of 13,843 lb. (6,279 kg.):* 507 miles (815 km.).

PROVIDER (U.S.A.)

22

Fairchild C-123B Provider of the Royal Thai Air Force, *ca* 1967-68. *Engines:* Two 2,500 h.p. Pratt & Whitney R-2800-99W Double Wasp eighteen-cylinder radials. *Span:* 110 ft. 0 in. (33.53 m.). *Length:* 76 ft. 3 in. (23.24 m.). *Wing area:* 1,223.0 sq. ft. (113.62 sq. m.). *Maximum take-off weight:* 60,000 lb. (27,216 kg.). *Maximum cruising speed:* 205 m.p.h. (330 km/hr.). at 5,000 ft. (1,525 m.). *Service ceiling:* 24,000 ft. (7,315 m.). *Range with payload of 16,000 lb. (7,257 kg.):* 1,650 miles (3,380 km.).

23

Hawker Siddeley Andover C. Mk 1 of No 46 Squadron, RAF Transport Command.
1968. *Engines:* Two 3,245 e.s.h.p. Rolls-Royce Dart RDa.12 Mk 201 turboprops.
Span: 98 ft. 3 in. (29.95 m.). *Length:* 78 ft. 0 in. (23.77 m.). *Wing area:* 831.4 sq. ft.
(77.20 sq. m.). *Maximum take-off weight:* 50,000 lb. (22,680 kg.). *Maximum
cruising speed:* 265 m.p.h. (426 km/hr.) at 15,000 ft. (4,570 m.). *Service ceiling:*
24,000 ft. (7,300 m.). *Range with payload of 8,530 lb. (3,870 kg.):* 1,158 miles
(1,865 km.).

TRANSALL C-160 (Germany/France)

24

Transall C-160 F of the 61e Escadre, Armée de l'Air, Orléans 1969. *Engines:* Two 6,100 e.s.h.p. Rolls-Royce Tyne RTy.20 Mk 22 turboprops. *Span:* 131 ft. 3 in. (40.00 m.). *Length:* 106 ft 3½ in. (32.40 m.). *Wing area:* 1,722.7 sq.ft. (160.10 sq.m.). *Maximum take-off weight:* 108,250 lb. (49,100 kg.). *Maximum cruising speed:* 319 m.p.h. (513 km/hr.) at 18,050 ft. (5,500 m.). *Service ceiling:* 27,900 ft. (8,500 m.). *Range with payload of 17,640 lb. (8,000 kg):* 2,832 miles (4,558 km.).

GREYHOUND (U.S.A.)

25

Grumman C-2A Greyhound of US Navy Squadron VRC-50, *ca* 1968. *Engines:*
Two 4,050 e.s.h.p. Allison T56-A-8/8A turboprops. *Span:* 80 ft. 7 in. (24.56 m.).
Length: 56 ft. 8 in. (17.27 m.). *Wing area:* 700.0 sq. ft. (65.03 sq. m.). *Maximum
take-off weight:* 54,830 lb. (24,870 kg.). *Maximum speed:* 352 m.p.h. (567 km/hr.)
at optimum altitude. *Service ceiling:* 28,800 ft. (8,870 m.). *Typical range:* 1,650
miles (2,660 km.).

NORATLAS (France)

26

Nord 2501 Noratlas of Lufttransportgeschwader 61, Federal German Luftwaffe, ca 1964. *Engines:* Two 2,040 h.p. SNECMA (Bristol) Hercules 758 fourteen-cylinder radials. *Span:* 106 ft 7½ in. (32.50 m.). *Length:* 72 ft. 0½ in. (21.96 m.). *Wing area:* 1,089.0 sq. ft. (101.20 sq. m.). *Maximum take-off weight:* 45,415 lb. (20,600 kg.). *Cruising speed:* 208 m.p.h. (335 km/hr.) at 9,840 ft. (3,000 m.). *Service ceiling:* 24,600 ft. (7,500 m.). *Range with payload of 14,990 lb. (6,800 kg.):* 1,710 miles (2,750 km).

27

North American OV-10A Bronco of the US Marine Corps, *ca* 1968. *Engines:* Two 715 s.h.p. AiResearch T76-G-10/12 turboprops. *Span:* 40 ft. 0 in. (12.19 m.). *Length:* 41 ft. 7 in. (12.67 m.). *Wing area:* 291.0 sq. ft. (27.03 sq. m.). *Normal take-off weight (clean):* 9,908 lb. (4,494 kg.). *Maximum speed:* 281 m.p.h. (452 km/hr.) at sea level. *Combat radius with maximum ordnance:* 228 miles (367 km.).

MOHAWK (U.S.A.)

28

Grumman OV-1B Mohawk of the US Army, 1966. *Engines:* Two 1,400 s.h.p. Lycoming T53-L-701 turboprops. *Span:* 48 ft. 0 in. (14.63 m.). *Length:* 41 ft. 0 in. (12.50 m.) excluding SLAR pod. *Wing area:* 360.0 sq. ft. (33.45 sq. m.). *Maximum take-off weight:* 19,230 lb. (8,722 kg.). *Maximum speed:* 297 m.p.h. (478 km/hr.) at 5,000 ft. (1,525 m.). *Service ceiling:* 30,300 ft. (9,235 m.). *Maximum range with underwing fuel tanks:* 1,230 miles (1,980 km.).

29

Grumman S-2A Tracker of No 2 Squadron, Koninklijke Marine Luchtvaartdienst, *ca* 1964-65. *Engines:* Two 1,525 h.p. Wright R-1820-82WA Cyclone nine-cylinder radials. *Span:* 69 ft. 8 in. (21.23 m.). *Length:* 42 ft. 3 in. (12.88 m.). *Wing area:* 485.0. sq. ft. (45.06 sq. m.). *Maximum take-off weight:* 26,300 lb. (11,930 kg). *Maximum speed:* 287 m.p.h. (462 km/hr.) at sea level. *Service ceiling:* 23,000 ft. (7,000 m.). *Maximum range:* 900 miles (1,450 km.)

ATLANTIC (France)

30

Breguet 1150 Atlantic of Marinefliegergruppe 3, Bundesmarine, *ca* 1967. *Engines:* Four 6,105 e.h.p. SNECMA-built Rolls-Royce Tyne RTy.20 Mk 21 turboprops. *Span:* 119 ft. 1 in. (36.30 m.). *Length:* 104 ft. 2 in. (31.75 m.). *Wing area:* 1,295.0 sq. ft. (120.34 sq.m.). *Maximum take-off weight:* 95,900 lb. (43,500 kg.). *Cruising speed:* 345 m.p.h. (556 km/hr.). *Service ceiling:* 32,800 ft. (10,000 m.). *Maximum range:* 5,590 miles (9,000 km.).

31

Beriev Be-12 of the Soviet Naval Air Force, *ca* 1967-8. *Engines:* Two 4,000 s.h.p.
Ivchenko AI-20 turboprops. *Span:* 97 ft. 6 in. (29.70 m.). *Length:* 99 ft. 0 in.
(30.20 m.). *Height:* 22 ft. 11½ in. (7.00 m.). *Maximum take-off weight:* 65,035 lb.
(29,500 kg.). *Maximum speed:* 379 m.p.h. (610 km/hr.). *Maximum range:* 2,485
miles (4,000 km.). *All data estimated.*

HAWKEYE (U.S.A.)

32

Grumman E-2A Hawkeye of US Navy Squadron VAW-111 (Detachment C), USS *Kitty Hawk, ca* 1967. *Engines:* Two 4,050 e.s.h.p. Allison T56-A-8/8A turboprops. *Span:* 80 ft. 7 in. (24.56 m.). *Length:* 56 ft. 4 in. (17.17 m.). *Wing area:* 700.0 sq.ft. (65.03 sq.m.). *Maximum take-off weight:* 49,638 lb. (22, 515 kg.). *Cruising speed:* 315 m.p.h. (508 km/hr.). *Service ceiling:* 31,700 ft. (9,660 m.). *Ferry range on internal fuel:* 1,905 miles (3,065 km.).

NEPTUNE (U.S.A.)

33

Kawasaki-built Lockheed P-2H (P2V-7) of the Japan Maritime Self Defence Force,
ca 1962. *Engines:* Two 3,500 h.p. Wright R-3350-32W Turbo-Compounds and
two 3,400 lb. (1,542 kg.) st. Westinghouse J34-WE-36 auxiliary turbojets. *Span
over tip-tanks:* 103 ft. 10 in. (31.65 m.). *Length:* 91 ft. 8 in. (27.94 m.). *Wing area:*
1,000.0 sq. ft. (92.90 sq. m.). *Maximum take-off weight:* 79,895 lb. (36,240 kg.).
Maximum speed: 356 m.p.h. (573 km/hr.) at 10,000 ft. (3,050 m.). *Service ceiling:*
22,000 ft. (6,700 m.). *Normal range:* 2,200 miles (3,540 km.).

ORION (U.S.A.)

34

Lockheed P-3B, first aircraft for the RNZAF, 1966. *Engines:* Four 4,910 e.s.h.p. Allison T56-A-14 turboprops. *Span:* 99 ft. 8 in. (30.37 m.). *Length:* 116 ft. 10 in. (35.61 m.). *Wing area:* 1,300.0 sq. ft. (120.77 sq. m.). *Maximum take-off weight:* 135,000 lb. (61,235 kg.). *Cruising speed:* 378 m.p.h. (608 km/hr.) at 25,000 ft. (7,620 m.). *Service ceiling:* 28,300 ft. (8,625 m.). *Operational radius:* 1,550 miles (2,495 km.).

35

Canadair CP-107 Argus 2 of Maritime Air Command, Royal Canadian Air Force,
ca 1962. *Engines:* Four 3,400 h.p. (3,700 h.p. with water injection) Wright R-3350-
EA-1 Turbo Compounds. *Span:* 142 ft. 3½ in. (43.37 m.). *Length:* 128 ft. 3 in.
(39.09 m.). *Wing area:* 2,075.0 sq. ft. (192.78 sq. m.) *Normal take-off weight:*
148,000 lb. (67,130 kg.). *Maximum speed:* 315 m.p.h. (507 km/hr.) at 20,000 ft.
(6,100 m.). *Service ceiling:* approx 25,000 ft. (7,620 m.). *Maximum range:* 5,900
miles (9,495 km.).

SHIN MEIWA PS-1 (Japan)

36

Shin Meiwa PX-S, second prototype in the insignia of
the Japan Maritime Self Defence Force, 1969. *Data
apply to pre-series PS-1.* Engines: Four 2,850 e.h.p.
Ishikawaima-built General Electric T64-IHI-10 turboprops. *Span:* 108 ft. 8¾ in. (33.14 m.). *Length:* 109 ft.
11 in. (33.50 m.). *Wing area:* 1,462.0 sq. ft. (135.80
sq.m.). *Maximum take-off weight:* 94,800 lb. (43,000
kg.). *Maximum speed:* 340 m.p.h. (547 km/hr.) at
5,000 ft. (1,525 m.). *Service ceiling:* 29,500 ft. (9,000
m.). *Normal range:* 1,347 miles (2,168 km.).

海上自衛隊

SUPER CONSTELLATION (U.S.A.)

37

Lockheed EC-121K Super Constellation of the US Navy Pacific Missile Range Squadron, Hawaii, *ca* 1963. *Engines:* Four 3,400 h.p. Wright R-3350-34 or-42 Turbo Compounds. *Span:* 123 ft. 5 in. (37.62 m.). *Length:* 116 ft. 2 in. (35.41 m.). *Wing area:* 1,654.0 sq. ft. (153.66 sq. m.). *Maximum take-off weight:* 143,600 lb. (65,135 kg.). *Maximum speed:* 321 m.p.h. (517 km/hr.) at 20,000 ft. (6,100 m.). *Service ceiling:* 20,600 ft. (6,280 m.). *Maximum range:* 4,600 miles (7,405 km.).

38

Hawker Siddeley Argosy C.Mk 1 of No 267 Squadron, RAF Transport Command, *ca* 1964-65. *Engines:* Four 2,680 e.s.h.p. Rolls-Royce Dart RDa.8 Mk 101 turboprops. *Span:* 115 ft. 0 in. (35.05 m.). *Length:* 89 ft. 2 in. (27.18 m.). *Wing area:* 1,458.0 sq. ft. (135.45 sq. m.). *Normal take-off weight:* 97,000 lb. (44,000 kg.). *Maximum cruising speed:* 269 m.p.h. (433 km/hr.) at 20,000 ft. (6,100 m.). *Range with payload of 20,000 lb. (9,072 kg.):* 1,070 miles (1,720 km.).

YUKON (Canada)

39

Canadair CC-106 Yukon of No 437 Squadron, Royal Canadian Air Force. *ca* 1962.
Engines: Four 5,730 e.s.h.p. Rolls-Royce Tyne Mk 515/10 turboprops. *Span:*
142 ft. 3½ in. (43.37 m.). *Length:* 136 ft. 10 in. (41.71 m.). *Wing area:* 2,075.0 sq. ft.
(192.78 sq. m.). *Maximum take-off weight:* 205,000 lb. (92,985 kg.). *Maximum
cruising speed:* 392 m.p.h. (631 km/hr.) at 20,000 ft. (6,100 m.). *Range with payload of 60,480 lb. (27,434 kg.):* 2,360 miles (3,798 km.).

BREGUET 941S (France)

40

Breguet 941S, first pre-production aircraft, in Armée de l'Air insignia, 1967. *Data correct to 1971. Engines:* Four 1,500 s.h.p. Turboméca Turmo IIID6 turboprops. *Span:* 76 ft. 8½ in. (23.40 m.). *Length:* 77 ft. 11 in. (23.75 m.). *Wing area:* 902.0 sq. ft. (83.78 sq. m.). *Typical take-off weight:* 52,580 lb. (23,850 kg.). *Maximum cruising speed:* 259 m.p.h. (417 km/hr.) at 10,000 ft. (3,050 m.). *Service ceiling:* 31,170 ft. (9,500 m.). *Range with maximum payload of 22,045 lb. (10,000 kg.)* 620 miles (1,000 km.).

HERCULES (U.S.A.)

41

Lockheed Hercules C. Mk 1 (C-130K) of No 242 OCU, RAF Transport Command, 1967. *Engines:* Four 4,500 e.s.h.p. (limited) Allison T56-A-15 turboprops. *Span:* 132 ft. 7 in. (40.41 m.). *Length:* 97 ft. 9 in. (29.78 m.). *Wing area:* 1,745.0 sq. ft. (162.12 sq. m.). *Maximum normal take-off weight:* 155,000 lb. (70,310 kg.) *Maximum cruising speed:* 375 m.p.h. (603 km/hr.). *Service ceiling:* 33,000 ft. (10,060 m.). *Range with payload of 45,525 lb. (20,650 kg):* 2,450 miles (3,945 km.).

ANTONOV An-12 (U.S.S.R.)

42

Antonov An-12 of the Iraqi Air Force, May 1969. *Engines:* Four 4,250 s.h.p. Ivchenko AI-20K turboprops. *Span:* 124 ft. 8 in. (38.00 m.). *Length:* 108 ft. 3 in. (33.00 m.). *Wing area:* 1,292.0 sq. ft. (120.00 sq. m.). *Normal take-off weight:* 119,050 lb. (54,000 kg.). *Maximum cruising speed:* 373 m.p.h. (600 km/hr.) *Service ceiling:* 33,500 ft. (10,200 m.). *Range with payload of 22,045 lb. (10,000 kg.):* 2,110 miles (3,400 km.).

BELFAST (U.K.)

43

Short Belfast C. Mk 1 of No 53 Squadron, RAF Transport Command, *ca* 1964. *Engines:* Four 5,730 e.s.h.p. Rolls-Royce Tyne RTy.12 Mk 101 turboprops. *Span:* 158 ft. 9½ in. (48.42 m.). *Length:* 136 ft. 5 in. (41.69 m.). *Wing area:* 2,466.0 sq. ft. (229.10 sq. m.). *Maximum take-off weight:* 230,000 lb. (104,300 kg.) *Maximum cruising speed:* 352 m.p.h. (566 km/hr.) at 24,000 ft. (7,300 m.). *Service ceiling:* 30,000 ft. (9,145 m.). *Range with maximum payload of 78,000 lb. (35,400 kg.):* 1,000 miles (1,610 km.).

CARGOMASTER (U.S.A.)

44

Douglas C-133B Cargomaster of Military Airlift Command, USAF, *ca* 1966. *Engines:* Four 7,500 e.s.h.p. Pratt & Whitney T34-P-9WA turboprops. *Span:* 179 ft. 8 in. (54.76 m.). *Length:* 157 ft. 6½ in. (48.02 m.). *Wing area:* 2,673.0 sq.ft. (248.33 sq.m.). *Maximum take-off weight:* 286,000 lb. (129,725 kg.). *Maximum cruising speed:* 323 m.p.h. (520 km/hr.) at 26,850 ft. (8,185 m.). *Service ceiling:* 29,950 ft. (9,130 m.). *Range with payload of 51,850 lb. (23,518 kg.):* 4,030 miles (6,485 km.).

ANTONOV An-22 (U.S.S.R.)

45

Antonov An-22 of the Soviet Air Force, 1970. *Engines:*
Four 15,000 s.h.p. Kuznetsov NK-12MA turboprops.
Span: 211 ft. 4 in. (64.40 m.). *Length:* approx 190 ft.
0 in. (57.91 m.). *Wing area:* 3,713.0 sq. ft. (345.00 sq.
m.). *Maximum take-off weight:* 551,160 lb. (250,000
kg.). *Maximum speed:* 460 m.p.h. (740 km/hr.). *Range
with payload of 99,200 lb. (45,000 kg.):* 6,800 miles
(10,950 km.).

TUPOLEV Tu-95 (U.S.S.R.)

Tupolev "Moss", airborne warning and control version of the Tu-114.

46

Tupolev Tu-95 Bear-B of the Soviet Air Force, *ca* 1963-64. *Engines:* Four 14,795 e.s.h.p. Kuznetsov NK-12M turboprops *Span:* 167 ft. 4 in. (51.00 m.). *Length:* 162 ft. 4¾ in. (49.50 m.). *Wing area:* 3,342.2 sq.ft. (310.50 sq. m.). *Maximum take-off weight:* 340,000 lb. (154,200 kg.). *Maximum speed:* 530 m.p.h. (850 km/hr.) at 41,000 ft. (12,500 m.). *Maximum range with 25,000 lb. (11,340 kg.) weapons load:* 7,800 miles (12,550 km.). *All data estimated.*

LOCKHEED U-2 (U.S.A.)

47
Lockheed WU-2A flown by Lockheed for the US Air Force Flight Dynamics Laboratory, *ca* 1964. *Engine:* One 11,200 lb. (5,080 kg.) st Pratt & Whitney J57-P-37A turbojet. *Span:* 80 ft. 0 in. (24.38 m.). *Length:* 49 ft. 7 in. (15.11 m.). *Wing area:* 565.0 sq. ft. (52.49 sq. m.). *Normal take-off weight:* 15,850 lb. (6,842 kg.). *Maximum speed:* 495 m.p.h. (797 km/hr.) at 40,000 ft. (12,200 m.). *Service ceiling:* 55,000 ft. (16,775 m.). *Range on internal fuel:* 2,200 miles (3,540 km.).

LOCKHEED SR-71 (U.S.A.)

48

Lockheed SR-71A of the 9th Strategic Reconnaissance Wing, USAF, Beale AFB (California), ça 1967-68. *Engines:* Two 32,500 lb. (14,740 kg.) st Pratt & Whitney J58 (JT11D-20B) afterburning turbojets. *Span:* 55 ft. 7 in. (16.95 m.). *Length:* 107 ft. 5 in. (32.74 m.). *Height:* 18 ft. 6 in. (5.64 m.). *Maximum take-off weight:* approx 170,000 lb. (77,110 kg.). *Maximum speed:* approx 2,300 m.p.h. (3,700 km/hr.) at high altitude. *Service ceiling:* over 80,000 ft. (24,400 m.). *Range:* approx 2,980 miles (4,800 km.).

BUCCANEER (U.K.)

49

Hawker Siddeley Buccaneer S.Mk 50 of No 24 Squadron, South African Air Force, Waterkloof (Pretoria), 1966. *Engines:* Two 11,100 lb. (5,035 kg.) st Rolls-Royce RB.168-1A Spey turbofans and one 8,000 lb. (3,630 kg.) st Rolls-Royce Bristol BS.605 rocket motor. *Span:* 44 ft. 0 in. (13.41 m.). *Length:* 63 ft. 5 in. (19.33 m.). *Wing area:* 514.7 sq. ft. (47.82 sq. m.). *Maximum take-off weight:* 62,000 lb. (28,123 kg.). *Maximum speed:* 645 m.p.h. (1,038 km/hr.) at 200 ft. (61 m.). *Typical operational range:* 2,300 miles (3,700 km.).

50

Grumman A-6A Intruder of US Navy Squadron VA-85, USS *America*, south-west Pacific area, *ca* 1968. *Engines:* Two 9,300 lb. (4,218 kg.) st Pratt & Whitney J52-P-8A turbojets. *Span:* 53 ft. 0 in. (16.15 m.). *Length:* 54 ft. 7 in. (16.64 m.). *Wing area:* 529.0 sq.ft. (49.15 sq. m.). *Maximum take-off weight:* 60.626 lb. (27,500 kg.). *Maximum speed:* 685 m.p.h. (1,102 km/hr.) at sea level. *Service ceiling:* 41,660 ft. (12,700 m.). *Typical combat range:* 1,920 miles (3,090 km.).

SKYHAWK (U.S.A.)

51

McDonnell Douglas A-4E Skyhawk of US Navy Squadron VA-56, USS *Ranger*, *ca* 1964. *Engine:* One 8,500 lb. (3,855 kg.) st Pratt & Whitney J52-P-6A turbojet. *Span:* 27 ft. 6 in. (8.38 m.). *Length:* 40 ft. 3¼ in. (12.27 m.). *Wing area:* 260.0 sq.ft. (24.16 sq.m.). *Maximum take-off weight:* 24,500 lb. (11,113 kg.). *Maximum speed:* 673 m.p.h. (1,083 km/hr.) at sea level. *Service ceiling:* 49,000 ft. (14,935 m.). *Range with auxiliary tanks:* 1,400 miles (2,253 km.).

52

North American RA-5C Vigilante of US Navy Squadron RVAH-5, USS *Ranger*, 1964. *Engines:* Two 10,900/17,000 lb. (4,944/7,711 kg.) st General Electric J79-GE-8 afterburning turbojets. *Span:* 53 ft. 0¼ in. (16.16 m.). *Length:* 75 ft. 10 in. (23.11 m.). *Wing area:* 769.0 sq. ft. (71.44 sq. m.). *Maximum take-off weight:* approx 80,000 lb. (36,287 kg.). *Maximum speed:* 1,385 m.p.h. (2,230 km/hr.) at 40,000 ft. (12,200 m.). *Service ceiling:* 64,000 ft. (19,500 m.). *Maximum range on internal fuel:* 3,000 miles (4,830 km.).

MIRAGE III-R (France)

53

Dassault Mirage III-R of the 3rd Escadron, 33rd Escadre, Armée de l'Air, Strasbourg *ca* 1966-67. *Engine:* One 9,430/13,670 lb. (4,280/6,200 kg.) st SNECMA Atar 09C afterburning turbojet. *Span:* 27 ft. 0 in. (8.22 m.). *Length:* 50 ft. 10¼ in. (15.50 m.) including probe. *Wing area:* 375.0 sq. ft. (34.85 sq. m.). *Maximum take-off weight:* 29,760 lb. (13,500 kg.). *Maximum speed:* 1,460 m.p.h (2,350 km/hr.) at 39,375 ft. (12,000 m.). *Service ceiling:* 55,775 ft. (17,000 m.). *Typical radius:* 745 miles (1,200 km.).

MIRAGE IV-A (France)

54

Dassault Mirage IV-A of the Commandement des Forces Aériennes Stratégiques ⊙ı the Armée de l'Air, *ca* 1965. *Engines:* Two 10,362/15,432 lb. (4,700/7,000 kg.) st SNECMA Atar 09K-50 afterburning turbojets. *Span:* 38 ft. 10½ in. (11.85 m.). *Length:* 77 ft. 1¼ in (23.50 m.). *Wing area:* 839.6 sq.ft. (78.00 sq. m.). *Typical take-off weight:* 69,665 lb. (31,600 kg.). *Maximum speed:* 1,454 m.p.h. (2,340 km/hr.) at 36,000 ft. (11,000 m.). *Service ceiling:* 65,600 ft. (20,000 m.). *Maximum range with external tanks:* 2,485 miles (4,000 km.).

TUPOLEV Tu-16 (U.S.S.R.)

55

Tupolev Tu-16 Badger-B of the Angkatan Udara Republik Indonesia, *ca* 1962.
Engines: Two 20,950 lb. (9,500 kg.) st Mikulin AM-3M turbojets. *Span:* 110 ft.
0 in. (33.50 m.). *Length:* 120 ft. 0 in. (36.50 m.). *Wing area:* approx 1,820.0 sq.ft.
(169.00 sq. m.). *Normal take-off weight:* approx 150,000 lb. (68,000 kg.). *Maximum
speed:* 587 m.p.h. (945 km/hr.) at 35,000 ft. (10,700 m.). *Service ceiling:* 42,650 ft.
(13,000 m.). *Range with 6,614 lb. (3,000 kg.) bomb load:* 3,975 miles (6,400 km.).

TUPOLEV Tu-22 (U.S.S.R.)

56

Tupolev Tu-22 Blinder-A of the Soviet Air Force, *ca* 1968. *Engines:* Two 26,000 lb.
(11,790 kg.) st afterburning turbojets of unknown type. *Span:* 90 ft. 10½ in. (27.70
m.). *Length:* 132 ft. 11½ in. (40.53 m.). *Wing area:* 2,045.0 sq.ft. (190.00 sq. m.).
Maximum take-off weight: 184,970 lb. (83,900 kg.). *Maximum speed:* 920 m.p.h.
(1,480 km/hr.) at 40,000 ft. (12,200 m.). *Service ceiling:* 60,000 ft. (18,300 m.).
Maximum range: 1,400 miles (2,250 km.). *All data estimated.*

SKYWARRIOR (U.S.A.)

57

Douglas A-3B Skywarrior of US Navy Squadron VAH-6, *ca* 1962. *Engines:* Two 12,400 lb. (5,624 kg.) st Pratt & Whitney J57-P-10 turbojets. *Span:* 72 ft. 6 in. (22.10 m.). *Length:* 76 ft. 4 in. (23.27 m.). *Wing area:* 812.0 sq. ft. (75.43 sq. m.). *Normal take-off weight:* 73,000 lb. (33,112 kg.). *Maximum speed:* 610 m.p.h. (982 km/hr.) at 10,000 ft. (3,050 m.). *Service ceiling:* 41,000 ft. (12,500 m.). *Operational radius:* 1,050 miles (1,690 km.).

58

Yakovlev Yak-28 Brewer of the Soviet Air Force, *ca* 1963. *Engines:* Two 9,480/
12,500 lb. (4,300/5,670 kg.) st Tumansky RD-11 afterburning turbojets.
Span: 42 ft. 6 in. (12.95 m.). *Length:* 71 ft. $0\frac{1}{2}$ in. (21.65 m.). *Wing area:* 410.0
sq. ft. (38.00 sq. m.). *Maximum take-off weight:* 35,275 lb. (16,000 kg.).
Maximum speed: 733 m.p.h. (1,180 km/hr.) at 36,000 ft. (11,000 m.). *Service
ceiling:* 55,775 ft. (17,000 m.). *Maximum combat radius:* 575 miles (925 km.).
All data estimated.

YAKOVLEV "MANDRAKE" (U.S.S.R.)

59

Yakovlev Mandrake of the Soviet Air Force, *ca* 1962. *Engines:* Two 5,512 lb. (2,500 kg.) st Klimov RD-9 turbojets. *Span:* 70 ft. 6½ in. (21.50 m.) *Length:* 50 ft. 0½ in. (15.25 m.). *Height:* 15 ft. 5 in. (4.70 m.). *Take-off weight:* 22,046 lb. (10,000 kg.). *Maximum speed:* 560 m.p.h. (900 km/hr.) at 39,375 ft. (12,000 m.). *Service ceiling:* 65,625 ft. (20,000 m.). *Range:* 2,485 miles (4,000 km.). *All data estimated.*

GENERAL DYNAMICS (MARTIN) RB-57F (U.S.A.)

60

General Dynamics (Martin) RB-57F of the 58th Weather Reconnaissance Squadron, USAF, during "Exercise Coldcat", Singapore, early 1969. *Engines:* Two 18,000 lb. (8,165 kg) st Pratt & Whitney TF33-P-11 turbofans and two 3,300 lb. (1,500 kg.) st Pratt & Whitney J60-P-9 auxiliary turbojets. *Span:* 122 ft 5 in. (37.32 m.). *Length:* 69 ft. 0 in (21.03 m.). *Wing area:* 2,000.0 sq.ft. (185.8 sq.m.). *Service ceiling:* approx 10,000 ft. (30,480 m.). *Maximum range:* approx 4,000 miles (6,440 km.). *All other data classified.*

KAWASAKI C-1 (Japan)

61

NAMC-built XC-1 first prototype in the insignia of the Japan Air Self Defence Force, 1970. *Engines:* Two 14,500 lb. (6,575 kg.) st Pratt & Whitney JT8D-9 turbofans. *Span:* 100 ft. 4¾ in (30.60 m.). *Length:* 95 ft. 1¾ in. (29.00 m.). *Wing area:* 1,297.0 sq. ft. (120.50 sq. m.). *Maximum take-off weight:* 85,320 lb. (38,700 kg.). *Maximum speed:* 512 m.p.h. (824 km/hr.) at 25,000 ft. (7,620 m.). *Service ceiling:* 42,500 ft. (12,950 m.). *Range with payload of 17,640 lb. (8,000 kg.):* 840 miles (1,350 km.).

62

Lockheed S-3A Viking, based on mock-up details released in 1970. Data correct to December 1971. *Engines:* Two approx 9,000 lb. (4,082 kg.) st General Electric TF34-GE-2 turbofans. *Span:* 68 ft. 8 in. (20.93 m.). *Length:* 53 ft. 4 in. (16.26 m.). *Wing area:* 598.0 sq. ft. (55.56 sq. m.). *Normal take-off weight (ASW):* 42,500 lb. (19,277 kg.) *Maximum cruising speed:* over 403 m.p.h. (649 km/hr.). *Service ceiling:* over 35,000 ft. (10,670 m.). *Ferry range:* more than 3,455 miles (5,560 km.).

FALCON (France)

63

Dassault Fan Jet Falcon (Mystère 20) of No 412(T) Squadron, Canadian Armed Forces, 1968-69. *Engines:* Two 4,125 lb. (1,870 kg.) st General Electric CF700-2C turbofans. *Span:* 53 ft. 6 in. (16.30 m.). *Length:* 56 ft. 3 in. (17.15 m.). *Wing area:* 441.3 sq.ft. (41.00 sq. m.). *Maximum take-off weight:* 26,455 lb. (12,000 kg.). *Maximum cruising speed:* 534 m.p.h. (860 km/hr.) at 25,000 ft. (7,620 m.). *Absolute ceiling:* 42,000 ft. (12,800 m.). *Range with payload of 1,600lb. (725 kg.):* 1,900 miles (3,050 km.).

64

BAC VC10 C. Mk 1 of No 10 Squadron RAF Air Support Command, Brize Norton,
1968. *Engines:* Four 21,800 lb. (9,888 kg.) st Rolls-Royce Conway RCo.43 turbofans. *Span:* 146 ft. 2 in. (44.55 m.). *Length:* 158 ft. 8 in. (48.36 m.) *Wing area:* 2,932.0
sq. ft. (272.40 sq. m.). *Maximum take-off weight:* 323,000 lb. (146,510 kg.).
Maximum cruising speed: 581 m.p h. (935 km/hr.) at 31,000 ft. (9,450 m.).
Service ceiling: 42,000 ft. (12,800 m.). *Range with maximum payload of 57,400
lb. (26,030 kg.):* 3,900 miles (6,275 km.).

VULCAN (U.K.)

65

Hawker Siddeley Vulcan B. Mk 2 of No 35 Squadron, Tengah (Singapore), 1967. *Engines:* Four 20,000 lb. (9,072 kg.) st Rolls-Royce Bristol Olympus 301 turbojets. *Span:* 111 ft. 0 in. (33.83 m.). *Length:* 99 ft. 11 in. (30.45 m.). *Wing area:* 3,964.0 sq. ft. (368.27 sq. m.). *Maximum take-off weight:* approx 190,000 lb. (86,180 kg.). *Maximum speed:* approx 620 m.p.h. (998 km/hr.) at 50,000 ft. (15,240 m.). *Service ceiling:* 65,000 ft. (19,800 .m.). *Low-level radius on internal fuel:* 1,725 miles (2,775 km.).

66

Handley Page Victor B. Mk 2 of No 139 Squadron, RAF Bomber Command, 1966.
Engines: Four 20,600 lb. (9,344 kg.) st Rolls-Royce Conway RCo.17 Mk 201 turbofans. *Span:* 120 ft. 0 in. (36.58 m.). *Length:* 114 ft. 11 in. (35.03 m.). *Wing area:* 2,597.0 sq. ft. (240.27 sq. m.). *Normal operational weight:* approx 200,000 lb. (90,720 kg.) *Maximum speed:* approx 615 m.p.h. (990 km/hr.) at 40,000 ft. (12,200 m.). *Service ceiling:* over 60,000 ft. (18,300 m.). *Typical operational radius:* 1,725 miles (2,775 km.).

STRATOFORTRESS (U.S.A.)

67
Boeing B-52G Stratofortress of the 93rd Bombing Wing, USAF, 1968. *Engines:* Eight 13,750 lb. (6,237 kg.) st Pratt & Whitney J57-P-43W turbojets. *Span:* 185 ft. 0 in. (56.39 m.). *Length:* 157 ft. 7 in. (48.03 m.). *Wing area:* 4,000.0 sq. ft. (371.61 sq. m.). *Maximum take-off weight:* 480,000 lb. (217,720 kg.). *Maximum speed:* 630 m.p.h. (1,014 km/hr.) at 40,000 ft. (12,200 m.). *Service ceiling:* 55,000 ft. (16,750 m.). *Range with maximum internal bomb load:* 8,000 miles (12,875 km.).

BOEING C-135 (U.S.A.)

68

Boeing C-135B of Military Airlift Command, USAF, *ca* 1966. *Engines:* Four 18,000 lb. (8,165 kg.) st Pratt & Whitney TF33-P-5 turbofans. *Span:* 130 ft. 10 in. (39.88 m.). *Length:* 134 ft. 6 in. (41.00 m.). *Wing area:* 2,433.0 sq. ft. (226.04 sq. m.). *Normal take-off weight:* 275,500 lb. (122,700 kg.) *Maximum cruising speed:* 604 m.p.h. (972 km/hr.) at 40,000 ft. (12,200 m.). *Service ceiling:* 45,000 ft. (13,725 m.). *Range with payload* of *54,000 lb. (24,495 kg.):* 4,625 miles (7,445 km.).

69

Hawker Siddeley Nimrod MR. Mk 1, first production aircraft, of No 201 Squadron RAF Kinloss, 1970. *Engines:* Four 11,500 lb. (5,217 kg.) st Rolls-Royce RB.168 Spey Mk 250 turbofans. *Span:* 114 ft. 10 in. (35.00 m.). *Length:* 126 ft. 9 in. (38.63 m.). *Wing area:* 2,121.0 sq. ft. (197.00 sq. m.). *Typical take-off weight:* 175,500 lb. (79,605 kg.). *Maximum cruising speed:* 575 m.p.h. (926 km/hr.) *Typical endurance:* 12 hours.

MYASISHCHEV Mya-4 (U.S.S.R.)

70

Myasishchev 201-M (modified Mya-4) as exhibited at Domodedovo, 1967. *Data (estimated) apply to standard Mya-4. Engines:* Four 19,180 lb. (8,700 kg.) st Mikulin AM-3D turbojets. *Span:* 170 ft. 7¼ in. (52.00 m.). *Length:* 162 ft. 4¾ in. (49.50 m.). *Wing area:* 3,229.17 sq. ft. (300.00 sq. m.). *Maximum take-off weight:* 352,750 lb. (160,000 kg.). *Maximum speed:* 559 m.p.h. (900 km/hr.) at 36,000 ft. (11,000 m.). *Service ceiling:* 39,375 ft. (12,000 m.). *Typical range:* 3,100 miles (5,000 km.).

STARLIFTER (U.S.A.)

71

Lockheed C-141A StarLifter of the 437th Military Air Wing, USAF, *ca* 1967. *Engines:* Four 21,000 lb. (9,525 kg.) st. Pratt & Whitney TF33-P-7 turbofans. *Span:* 159 ft. 11 in. (48.74 m.). *Length:* 145 ft. 0 in. (44.20 m.). *Wing area:* 3,228.0 sq. ft. (299.9 sq. m.). *Maximum take-off weight:* 316,600 lb. (143,600 kg.) *Maximum cruising speed:* 564 m.p.h. (908 km/hr.) at 24,250 ft. (7,400 m.). *Service ceiling:* 41,600 ft. (12,680 m.). *Range with maximum payload of 70,847 lb. (32,136 kg.):* 4,080 miles (6,565 km.).

GALAXY (U.S.A.)

72
Lockheed C-5A Galaxy prototype in the insignia of Military Airlift Command, USAF, 1969. *Data apply to production version. Engines:* Four 41,000 lb. (18,600 kg.) st General Electric TF39-GE-1 turbofans *Span:* 222 ft 8½ in. (67.88 m.). *Length:* 247 ft. 10 in. (75.54 m.). *Wing area:* 6,200.0 sq. ft. (576.00 sq. m.). *Maximum take-off weight:* 728,000 lb. (330,200 kg.) *Typical cruising speed:* 507 m.p.h. (815 km/hr.). *Service ceiling:* 34,000 ft. (10,360 m.). *Range with payload of 220,000 lb. (99,790 kg.):* 3,510 miles (5,650 km.).

73

General Dynamics (Convair) B-58A Hustler of the Flight Test Center, Systems Command, USAF, *ca* 1964. *Engines:* Four 10,000/15,600 lb. (4,536/7,076 kg.) st General Electric J79-GE-5B afterburning turbojets. *Span:* 56 ft. 10 in. (17.32 m.). *Length:* 96 ft. 9 in. (29.49 m.). *Wing area:* 1,542.0 sq. ft. (143.25 sq. m.). *Maximum take-off weight:* 164,500 lb. (74,616 kg.). *Maximum speed:* 1,385 m.p.h. (2,230 km/hr.) at 44,000 ft. (13,400 m.). *Service ceiling:* 60,000 ft. (18,300 m.). *Typical combat radius:* 1,200 miles (1,930 km.).

1 Antonov An-2 ('Colt')

Produced in considerable numbers over a post-war period of more than 20 years, the An-2 is far from being the anachronism that might be supposed. On the contrary, the choice of a biplane configuration has many advantages for the range of duties that the An-2 has been required to perform during its long and varied career. In particular, the large wing area within a short span contributes to good STOL characteristics and good slow-speed handling, both eminently desirable in an aeroplane intended for use from small unprepared airstrips. The An-2 was originally designed, under the designation SKh-1 (Selskokhozyaistvenny = Agricultural Economic), for such operations as crop-spraying and pest control, and the prototype, powered by a 760 hp Shvetsov ASh-21 radial engine, was flown for the first time on 31 August 1947. This engine was retained in the first few production aircraft, but almost all An-2's built subsequently have had the 1,000 hp ASh-62IR. Soviet production, which began in 1948, had exceeded five thousand by 1960; since then the An-2 production centre has been the WSK factory at Mielec in Poland. The An-2 was also built in substantial quantities in the Chinese People's Republic. The standard personnel transport version, for both civil and military use, is the An-2P, which can accommodate 10–14 persons. Other variants include the agricultural An-2S (An-2R in Poland), the An-2ZA for high-altitude weather research, the An-2L water-bomber, and twin-float An-2V (An-2M in Poland). A modified agricultural version with enlarged vertical tail surfaces, the An-2M, was built in limited numbers in the USSR. The civil versions are described in the *Private, Business and General Purpose Aircraft since 1946* volume in this series; in military service, the An-2P is employed extensively by the A-VDV arm of the Soviet Air Force as a light passenger or freight transport (Polish designations of this version are An-2T and An-2TP), ambulance aircraft (Polish designation An-2S), radio and navigation trainer, and glider tug. Many, like the example illustrated, are used by the DOSAAF for parachute training. Polish designation of this version is An-2TD. Outside of the Soviet Union, military An-2's have also been supplied to the air arms of Afghanistan, Albania, Bulgaria, Cambodia, Cuba, Czechoslovakia, Egypt, the German Democratic Republic, Hungary, Iraq, the Korean Democratic People's Republic, Mongolia, Romania, Syria, North Vietnam, the Yemen and Yugoslavia. Some An-2's have given way to a later Antonov design, the An-14 monoplane, but such replacement is not thought to be widespread, and the older type continues in large-scale service, having now established an even longer production and service career than the Po-2 biplane which it was designed to replace.

2 Neiva Regente

Built by the Sociedade Construtora

Aeronáutica Neiva Ltda of São José dos Campos, the Regente bears a broad superficial resemblance to the Cessna Model 150 and is used by the Fôrça Aérea Brasileira as a 4-seat utility and AOP aircraft. The civil-registered first prototype (PP-ZTP) was flown on 7 September 1961, and was designated Model 360C by the manufacturer. This was placed in production as the U-42 (later C-42) for the Brazilian Air Force, for whom a total of eighty were built with 210 hp Continental IO-360-D flat-six engines. The first production Regente was flown in February 1965, and delivery of the initial production version was completed by the end of 1968. Meanwhile, in October 1967 Neiva had flown the YL-42 prototype (3120), intended to replace the Brazilian Air Force's L-6 Paulistinha and Cessna O-1 Bird Dog lightplanes in the AOP, liaison and observation roles. This differed from the C-42 chiefly in having a Lycoming O-360-A engine and a cut-down rear fuselage, with glazing at the rear of the cabin to improve the all-round view. Manufacturer's designation of the L-42 is Model 420L. Forty production L-42's were ordered for the Brazilian Air Force, the first of them flying in June 1969 and the last being delivered in March 1971. Provision is made in this version for four underwing attachments for light bombs, rockets or other stores.

3 Helio Super Courier
The Super Courier can trace its ancestry back to the 2-seat, 65 hp Helioplane, first flown on 8 April 1949 and itself based on the Piper Vagabond. The idea behind the design was to produce a lightplane with particularly good STOL and low-speed handling qualities, and from the original Helioplane evolved by Dr Otto Koppen and Mr Lynn Bollinger were subsequently developed a succession of later models which included the H-391 Courier (first flown 1952), H-392 Strato-Courier (1957) and H-395 Super Courier. The last-named was a 4/5-seat aircraft, and was first flown in 1958. Later that year three Super Couriers were evaluated by the USAF under the designation L-28A. In 1962, when the US adopted a new designation system common to all three services, these became known as U-10A's, and an additional quantity was ordered for 'special military duties' with Strategic and Tactical Air Commands. In the following year orders were placed by the US Army (twenty) and the Air National Guard (twenty-four). The standard USAF version is still the U-10A, but later versions are the U-10B and U-10D. Both have greater range than the U-10A; the U-10B, fitted with paratroop doors, has a maximum endurance of more than 10 hours, and the U-10D can seat six passengers in addition to the pilot. Super Courier operations in Southeast Asia have included leaflet-dropping, sky-shouting and other psychological warfare activities, and the dropping of medical supplies and comforts to beleaguered South Vietnamese communities.

4 Lockheed YO-3A

Airlines and their customers are not alone in their desire to acquire aircraft which are extremely quiet to operate. Reconnaissance is one military activity in which near-silent aircraft would possess an obvious advantage, and when the US authorities stated such a requirement officially in the mid-1960s Lockheed evolved a design known as the QT-2. Two of these aircraft – their designation signifies 'Quiet Thruster, 2-seat' – were built, the first of them making its first flight in August 1967. Basis of the design was the Schweizer SGS 2-32 sailplane, allied to a silenced engine driving a large-diameter, slow-turning propeller. Both QT-2's, fitted with night sensor equipment, were evaluated in Vietnam, where, it is claimed, they were able to make reconnaissance flights in 1968 at altitudes as low as 100 ft (30 m) without being detected. As a result of these operational trials, Lockheed then built a private-venture prototype of a more advanced version known as the Q-Star, which first flew in June 1968. Apart from modifying and strengthening the airframe, Lockheed also eventually replaced its original 100 hp Continental engine with a 200 hp (derated to 185 hp) Wankel rotary engine, making the Q-Star the first aeroplane in the USA to fly with a powerplant of this type. The engine is mounted aft of the cockpit, driving a large front-turning propeller by means of an extension shaft.

Only a month after the Q-Star's first (piston-engined) flight, the US Army awarded Lockheed a development contract which has led to a third stage in the development of a quiet reconnaissance aircraft. Like its predecessors, the YO-3A also uses the SGS 2-32 sailplane airframe as a basis, though the fuselage has been extensively altered and the wings are now located in the low position. The large canopy covers tandem cockpits for the 2-man crew, and infra-red night reconnaissance equipment is installed. The illustration shows the YO-3A in its initial configuration; later photographs released of the type undergoing evaluation in Vietnam show that the chord has been extended to the rear on the inner half of each wing, and that the original six-blade propeller has been replaced by a three-bladed one with larger blades.

5 Douglas A-1 Skyraider

The Skyraider may perhaps be said to have had greatness thrust upon it, for it was due for retirement after 5 years of service with the US Navy when the Korean war broke out in 1950. Its record during the next 3 years' conflict, and its amazing versatility, combined to keep it in continued production until 1957 when, after a 12-year run, the Douglas factories had turned out three thousand one hundred and eighty Skyraiders. Rather more than half of these were accounted for by the first five models (including one thousand and fifty-one A-1D's), which had passed out of front-line service by the mid-1960s; the remainder comprised six hundred and seventy A-1E's, seven hundred and thirteen A-1H's, and seventy-two A-1J's. The A-1E was primarily a 2-seat attack bomber, but capable of being converted by a ready-made kit system to night attack, early warning, ECM (EA-1E), 12-seat transport, 4-litter ambulance, 2,000 lb (907 kg) freighter, photographic reconnaissance or target towing duties. The A-1H is a single-seat low-altitude attack bomber, the A-1J being similar except for a higher-powered engine and an airframe strengthened to carry a tremendous variety of loads. The Skyraider's load-carrying capacity is one of its most remarkable features, and has played a major part in the success of this aeroplane under operational conditions. The specification to which it was designed called for a load of 1,000 lb (454 kg), but Skyraiders have flown regularly with more than 8,000 lb (3,630 kg) of external ordnance, and the type has been flown with more than 14,000 lb (6,350 kg) of underwing stores – greater than the aeroplane's own basic empty weight. The Skyraider's variety of load is equally impressive, and is augmented by four 20 mm wing cannon. Skyraiders had been withdrawn from US Navy service by the end of 1967, but in 1971 the USAF still operated several squadrons in Vietnam, and the South Vietnamese Air Force was also equipped with three squadrons of A-1E's and A-1H's. Other Skyraiders in the Far East at that time included about a dozen A-1D's,

which were resold by France in 1965 to the air force of Cambodia.

6 Breguet Alizé (Tradewind)

There are various schools of thought about the accomplishment of the basic functions of 'detect, classify, kill' involved in anti-submarine warfare. One, as practised by the US Navy, finds its answer in large twin-engined types such as the Grumman Tracker; another favours smaller, single-engined aircraft like the Gannet or Alizé. To pack all the radar and electronic gear for finding the modern submarine, and the weapons to attack it, into a modest-sized airframe, and still leave room for the engine, a 3-man crew and normal carrier equipment, is no easy task, yet it has been done in the Alizé without resorting to a large, fixed external radome such as is employed in many larger aircraft. The Alizé actually derives from the mixed-powerplant Vultur strike aircraft designed in 1948, although the first true Alizé prototype did not fly until 6 October 1956. A second prototype and three pre-production Alizés were followed by seventy-five production aircraft for the Aéronavale, the first of which was flown on 26 March 1959, and twelve for the Indian Navy. The latter, delivered in 1961, serve with 310 Squadron aboard the carrier *Vikrant*, while those in French service (since 1959) equip Flottilles 4F, 6F and 9F aboard the *Foch* and the *Clémenceau*. About half of the original number remained in service in 1971, but were being gradually replaced by SA 321G Super Frelon helicopters for the ASW role. The Alizé's CSF search radar is in a retractable 'dustbin' housing. Aft of this is the internal weapons bay, which has space for a homing torpedo or three 160 kg depth charges; and two similar or 175 kg charges, two Nord AS.12 or SS.11 missiles, or six 5 in aerial rockets can be suspended under-wing. The large 'knuckle' fairings on the wing leading edges house the retracted main landing gear; endurance of the Alizé is $3\frac{1}{2}$ to 4 hours.

7 Westland (Fairey) Gannet

The first Gannets, the anti-submarine Mk 1's, began to serve with the Fleet Air Arm in 1955, and were joined in the following year by the more powerful AS. Mk 4, total production of these two versions being about two hundred and fifty. Corresponding versions for ASW and radar observer training were the T.2 and T.5 respectively, and with modifications to incorporate more advanced electronics, some AS.4's were redesignated AS.6 and AS.7. The Gannet no longer performs front-line anti-submarine duties with the Royal Navy, and the fifteen AS.4's of the Federal German Bundesmarine have been replaced by Breguet Atlantics. The Royal Australian Navy still maintains one squadron of AS.4's aboard HMAS *Melbourne,* and Indonesia's naval air arm, the Angkatan Laut Republik Indonesia, has one shore-based squadron. On 20 August 1958, there took place the first flight of a much-redesigned Gannet, the AEW Mk 3, which is an all-weather early

warning aircraft. Carrying a pilot and two radar operators, the Gannet 3 has an entirely new fuselage, an enormous 'guppy' radome under the belly, a more powerful Mamba engine, enlarged vertical tail surfaces and provision for underwing drop-tanks. Forty-three Mk 3's were built, the first production example being flown on 2 December 1958. These aircraft were delivered to No 849 Squadron, whose motto, appropriately, is *Primus Video* – 'I see first'. This squadron, based at RNAS Brawdy in Scotland, maintains four flights, providing early warning cover for Royal Navy carriers. A feature of all marks of the Gannet, unique among service aircraft, is the Double Mamba turbo-prop engine. Fundamentally, this comprises two engines driving a single propeller shaft, and either component can be shut down while the other is used for cruising. This gives the aircraft – particularly when auxiliary drop-tanks are carried – an extremely useful patrol radius from its base. Overall Gannet production amounted to three hundred and seventy-eight aircraft, of which fifty-two were to meet export orders. A further eighteen ex-Royal Navy aircraft were also exported.

8 Cessna O-2

Cessna's first CLT (centre-line thrust) aircraft to fly was the Model 336 Skymaster, which made its first flight on 28 February 1961. Between then and January 1965, one hundred and ninety-five Skymasters were built before giving way to the much-improved Model 337 Super

Skymaster with restyled rear nacelle, fully-retractable landing gear and considerably superior performance. One of the attractions of the Model 337 (see the *Private Aircraft* volume in this series) is its low operating noise level, and this was no doubt a factor in the USAF decision of 1966 to replace its O-1 Bird Dog FAC (Forward Air Controller) aircraft by the later Cessna type. The initial military version, designated O-2A, seats up to 6 people, has full dual controls and is fitted with four underwing attachments for gun pods, rocket launchers, photo-flares or other stores. Two hundred and ninety-nine O-2A's have been ordered by the USAF, and twelve have been supplied to the Imperial Iranian Air Force for liaison, observation and training. A psychological warfare version, designated O-2B, is basically similar but carries advanced systems for communications, air-to-ground broadcasting and leaflet dropping. Thirty-one were produced for the USAF by converting commercial Model 337's, delivery of these beginning in March 1967. Reims Aviation in France, which licence-builds and markets the commercial 337, produced in 1970 the prototype of a military STOL version known as the FTMA-Milirole; the initials stand for France Turbo Militaire ADAC (Avion de Décollage et Aterrissage Court). This aircraft was flown for the first time on 26 May 1970 and is fitted with larger-area flaps which substantially improve the take-off and landing performance.

9 Britten-Norman BN-2A Islander and Defender

First flown on 13 June 1965, the 10-seat Britten-Norman Islander has since become one of the world's most successful and popular third-level and commuter transport aircraft, with more than three hundred examples sold by mid-1971. The Islander and its three-engined derivative, the Trislander, are fully described in the *Airliners since 1946* volume in this series. A small number of Islanders have also been sold to military customers, including the Abu Dhabi Defence Force (three), Guyana Defence Force (two), Iraqi Air Force (three) and Mexican Air Force (three). These are virtually standard BN-2A's, and are employed for a variety of tasks including personnel transport, communications, liaison and patrol or 'policing' duties. In 1971 Britten-Norman first revealed a new version, known as the Defender. With local strengthening of the airframe and other minimal changes, this can be utilised as a light attack aircraft, with four underwing pylons carrying a maximum 2,300 lb (1,043 kg) external load of gun or rocket pods, photo-flares, practice bombs or auxiliary fuel tanks. A 30 mile (48 km) range nose-mounted radar is standard, permitting the Defender to take advantage of its 10-hour endurance to conduct search and rescue missions, and the internal layout can be modified for paradropping, ambulance or aerial survey use.

10 Piaggio P.166

Existence of the Piaggio P.166 twin-engined feeder-line/ executive transport was first announced in March 1957, and the prototype (I-RAIF) made its first flight on 26 November of that year. Basically, the design represented a scaling-up of the Italian company's P.136 amphibian, retaining the latter's gull wing configuration combined with an enlarged landplane fuselage instead of the flying-boat hull. The P.166's commercial career is described in the *Private Aircraft* volume; fifty-one were built as P.166M's for the Aeronautica Militare Italiano. Nine also serve with No 27 Squadron of the SAAF as Albatross coastal patrol aircraft. The IAF P.166M's are used for light tactical transport, communications, ambulance work and training. The IAF began to receive, in 1972, the first of twenty P.166S's, a search and surveillance version with nose radar.

11 Mitsubishi MU-2

Design work on the MU-2, Mitsubishi's first entry into the executive/ feeder-liner market, began in 1959, and the first of three flying prototypes (JA 8620) made its maiden flight on 14 September 1963 powered by two 562 shp Turboméca Astazou IIK turboprop engines. Initial production version, from 1965, was the AiResearch-engined MU-2B, and since then a succession of different models have appeared of which the latest, up to early 1972, was the MU-2K. Total sales of all MU-2 versions had by then reached two hundred and forty, of which twenty-seven were for the Japanese armed forces: ten MU-2C's for the Ground Self Defence Force and sixteen MU-2E's for the Air Self Defence Force. The MU-2C, which has the JGSDF designation LR-1, was first flown on 11 May 1967, with delivery beginning at the end of the following month. It is basically similar to the commercial MU-2B, but with an unpressurised fuselage and (on one aircraft) an extra fuselage fuel tank instead of wingtip tanks. The LR-1's are used for liaison and reconnaissance/support duties, aircraft for the latter role having provision for a pair of 13 mm nose machine-guns, a light load of bombs or rockets, and either reconnaissance cameras or sideways-looking radar. The MU-2E, designated MU-2S by the JASDF, is an unpressurised search and rescue version distinguishable by its 'thimble' nose radome, bulged rear observation windows, and a sliding port-side door for lifeboat-dropping. It first flew on 15 August 1967.

12 Beagle Basset

When the Beagle company was formed in 1960, most of its early offerings were revisions or adaptations of earlier Auster designs. The first entirely new design to appear was the Beagle B.206X, which flew for the first time on 15 August 1961, powered by two 260 hp Continental IO-470-A engines, and from this was developed the slightly larger Basset CC.Mk 1 for the RAF. The Ministry of Aviation ordered two pre-production aeroplanes, with more powerful GIO-470 engines, which Beagle designated B.206Z1 and Z2, and the second of these became the Basset prototype, making its maiden flight on 20 February 1964. Twenty production B.206R Bassets followed, for service with the RAF's Southern and Northern Communications Flights, the first of these flying on 24 December 1964, and the remainder being delivered during 1965. These handsome little aeroplanes augmented, and eventually replaced, the RAF's Devons and few surviving Ansons on communications and light personnel transport duties. The Basset has a slightly larger rear door than the civil B.206 Series I, and seats up to 8 people, including the pilot(s).

13 **Beechcraft U-21**
First of the post-war Beech 'twins' adopted by the US armed forces was the Twin-Bonanza, four of which were acquired by the US Army as YL-23's for evaluation in 1952. Subsequent contracts covered fifty-five L-23A's, forty L-23B's, eighty-five L-23D's and six L-23E's, to which the name Seminole was applied. Most of the A and B models were later brought up to D standard, and in 1962 the L-23D and L-23E were redesignated U-8D and U-8E respectively. The U-8F (originally L-23F) was a developed version with a larger fuselage, and was based on the Model 65 Queen Air; three pre-series and sixty-eight production examples were completed for the US Army, and others were supplied to the Japan Mari-

time Self Defence Force (twenty-nine) and the air forces of Uruguay and Venezuela (six).

On 22 June 1961 Beech flew the prototype of a new and improved Queen Air, the Model 65–80, with 380 hp IGSO-540-A1A engines and a sweptback fin and rudder; this in turn was superseded by the Model 65-A80, with a 5 ft 0 in (1·52 m) increase in wing span, enlarged nose section and higher gross weight. From the remodelled Queen Air was developed the military U-21, principally to provide the US Army with a new light transport and utility aircraft for use in South-east Asia. A prototype was evaluated in 1963, and deliveries of the production U-21A (corresponding to the commercial Model 65-A90-1) began in May 1967. One hundred and twenty-four were ordered, followed by three U-21B's and two U-21C's; these are all in service and all have 550 shp PT6A-20 engines. Standard utility transport version is the U-21A, accommodating a crew of 2 and up to ten passengers or 3 stretchers. The RU-21A and electronics reconnaissance RU-21D are 'special-purpose' models. With 620 shp PT6A-29 engines and a gross weight of 10,900 lb (4,944 kg) the aircraft is known as the RU-21B (= Model 65-A90-2) and RU-21C (= Model 65-A90-3); the RU-21E is an electronics reconnaissance version of the Model 65-A90-4, of which sixteen were ordered in 1970, and the U-21F a pressurised development of the U-21A, of which five were ordered in 1971. Also delivered in 1971 were seventeen U-21G's

14 CASA 207 Azor

The Azor was the third general transport to come from the modest-sized Spanish aircraft industry since the war. The small CASA 201 Alcotan, which served in both military and civil roles, was followed by the CASA 202 Halcon, and the Azor was, in essence, an enlarged version of the Halcon. It was intended originally for the civil market, gaining its C of A in January 1958, the prototype having flown for the first time on 28 September 1955. The Spanish government, however, decided to order an initial batch of ten for the Ejército del Aire, by whom they are designated T.7A. These aircraft carry a crew of 4 and up to 40 passengers, and began to enter service with the Aviación de Trasporte in 1960. Two were fitted with 2,400 hp Pratt & Whitney Double Wasp radial engines, but the Hercules 730 is the standard powerplant. The Azor was intended to replace the CASA 352-L (Ju 52/3m), though the latter type remained in service for a time. A further ten Azors were subsequently ordered, these being designated T.7B and serving as freight transports. They can be distinguished from the T.7A version by the large cargo door at the rear of the fuselage.

15 Douglas C-47 Skytrain

Such has been the universal presence of the DC-3, in both military and commercial service, during and since World War 2 that one is apt to forget that it was already a major airliner by 1938, the prototype having flown for the first time in December 1935. More than 35 years later it is still a workhorse of a considerable number of small airlines the world over, and serves with the air arms of more than fifty nations, from Argentina to Yugoslavia. It would be near-impossible to estimate the total number still operating, but it probably runs into several thousand of the nearly eleven thousand that were built in the USA. What is perhaps an even greater tribute to this supremely adaptable aeroplane is that more than a dozen variants were still actively employed by the United States' own forces in the late 1960s, including some employed in Vietnam as AC-47 ground attack aircraft. With three General Electric 7·62 mm Miniguns firing 18,000 rounds per minute from the portside doorways, the AC-47 is euphemistically referred to by its crews as 'Puff, the magic dragon', among other titles. In its basic transport configuration the C-47 nominally has accommodation for a 7,500 lb (3,400 kg) cargo load or 28 troops, but in wartime it is known to have successfully, if not comfortably, carried at least 74 men. A considerable number of Lisunov Li-2's (the Russian licence version) remain active with many pro-Soviet states. The so-called 'Super DC-3', which has redesigned, square-cut wing and tail surfaces, uprated engines and other improvements, is also in service under C-117D series designations (formerly R4D-8). Ninety-eight were converted for service with the US Navy and Marine Corps.

16 Fokker-VFW Troopship

Few students of present-day civil aviation will require introduction to the Fokker Friendship airliner which, in its own field of short- to medium-range passenger operation, has been the most successful turbo-prop-engined civil transport produced anywhere in the world. Since the flight of the first prototype on 24 November 1955, several hundreds have been built for airline and private customers, both by Fokker in Holland and by Fairchild in the United States. The Philippine Air Force has one Mk 100 Friendship in service as a VIP transport, and three others serve with the Netherlands' own air force. In addition to these, however, there is a specialised military version known as the Troopship, which differs from the airliner models in having a big cargo-loading door in the forward port side of the fuselage, an enlarged paratroop door on each side aft, and a reinforced floor to take military loads. A maximum cargo load of 13,286 lb (6,025 kg) can be carried by the Troopship, and in less than 24 man-hours its internal layout can be converted from the cargo configuration to accommodate up to 45 paratroops, or 24 casualty stretchers plus seats for 9 orderlies or sitting patients. Nine Mk 300 Troopships, together with the three Friendships already mentioned, were delivered to No 334 Squadron of the Koninklijke Luchtmacht, two subsequently being converted as NASARR trainers. Sales of Mk 400 and Mk 600 Troopships (the latter does not have reinforced flooring) have subsequently been made to the air forces of Argentina (eight, plus four Friendships), Iran (ten, plus four Friendships), the Ivory Coast (one, plus one Friendship), Nigeria (four, plus two Friendships) and Sudan (four). In addition, two examples of the stretched FH-227B version, built by Fairchild, have been supplied to the Uruguayan Ministry of Defence.

17 Handley Page Herald

Handley Page's original Herald, which appeared in the mid-1950s and was powered by four Leonides Major piston engines, met with little success. When, however, twin Rolls-Royce Dart turboprops took the place of this powerplant in 1958, the aeroplane's fortunes somewhat improved, although total orders were still modest and took some time to accrue. The most widely used civil version was the Series 200, which is $3\frac{1}{2}$ ft (1·07 m) longer than the original Series 100, and from the former was developed the only military version to be ordered. This is the Series 400, and eight Herald Model 401's were delivered to equip one squadron of the Royal Malaysian Air Force in 1964–65. They differ from the Series 200 principally in having side-loading doors in the rear fuselage, and a reinforced floor. The military Herald can accommodate 50 fully-equipped troops or an equivalent freight load (which can be palletised for air-dropping), or, as a casualty evacuation aircraft, 24 stretchers and the requisite medical attendants.

18 FMA I.A.50 GII

Development of this multi-purpose military transport began early in 1960 when, after abandoning the earlier I.A.47 project for a 12/14-seat piston-engined feeder-liner, the Fabrica Militar de Aviones in Argentina began instead to study the possibilities of a turboprop-powered development of the I.A.35 Huanquero. The outcome of this was the prototype Guarani I (LQ-HER, originally known as Constancia II), which retained much of the basic Huanquero airframe but was given a lengthened fuselage and was powered by two 870 shp Turboméca Bastan IIIA turboprop engines. The twin-tailed Guarani I was flown for the first time on 6 February 1962, and designs were completed for both military transport and 10-seat executive transport versions. However, some 5 months earlier a third design had also been completed, this having 930 shp Bastan VI engines, a shortened rear fuselage and a single sweptback fin and rudder. This version, known as the I.A.50 Guarani II, first flew in prototype form (LV-X27) on 23 April 1963, followed by a second prototype (TX-01) and one pre-production machine. An initial batch of eighteen Guarani II's was ordered, the first six of which were delivered to the Fuerza Aérea Argentina between May and December 1966. Fourteen of these eighteen (serial numbers T-111 to T-124) were allocated as troop transports to I Air Brigada at El Palomar; the other four comprise two equipped for aerial photography and survey work (F-31 and F-32), one VIP transport for the FAA (TX-110) and one staff transport (5-T-30) for the Aviación Naval. Four other Guarani II's (the designation was altered to GII in 1970–71) were built for photographic duties with the Instituto Geográfico Militar, and one was completed as a Presidential transport. These twenty-three production aircraft are being followed by a further fifteen, ordered in October 1969, which have a lightened structure and redesigned interiors. The standard military transport version can accommodate, in addition to the 2-man crew, up to 15 paratroops or 6 stretchers and 2 medical attendants.

19 EMBRAER EMB-110 Bandeirante

The first indigenous transport aircraft design to emerge from the expanding Brazilian aircraft industry, the Bandeirante originated as the IPD/PAR-6504, designed to a Ministry of Aeronautics specification by the PAR-Departamento de Aeronaves of the Centro Técnico Aeroespacial under the initial guidance of the French aircraft designer Max Holste. The first of three YC-95 prototypes (2130) made its first flight on 26 October 1968, followed by the second (2131) on 19 October 1969 and the third (PP-ZCN) on 26 June 1970. These aircraft were powered by 550 shp PT6A-20 turboprop engines and had circular cabin windows. The fourth Bandeirante, which is representative of the production version, has more powerful PT6A-27 engines, modified nose, flight deck and cabin window contours, an additional cabin window in each side and a lengthened fuselage, as depicted in the colour plate. It was due to fly in the summer of 1972, and will be utilised for the structural test programme; the next three C-95's were due for completion by the end of the year. The Brazilian Air Force was expected to order up to eighty, subject to confirmation, as replacements for its ageing fleet of about fifty Beechcraft C-45's. The Bandeirante carries a crew of 2, and the main cabin has accommodation for 10–12 passengers.

20 De Havilland Canada DHC-4 Caribou

De Havilland Canada's avowed intent, in designing the Caribou, was to bridge the gap between the helicopter and the conventional transport, producing an aeroplane combining the payload of the latter with a first-class STOL airfield performance. Its success in achieving this objective has been borne out by the experience, under operational conditions, of the Caribou's extended use by the UNEF in the Middle East and the Congo, and by the US and Australian forces in Vietnam. Its excellent STOL characteristics, which make it independent of prepared airstrips, enable it to operate in either jungle or desert terrain, a factor amply supported by the sources of the orders for three hundred and seven aircraft which were subsequently placed,

nearly all for military versions. These have come from the US Army (one hundred and fifty-nine), and from the armed forces or governments of Abu Dhabi (five), Australia (thirty-one), Cameroun (two), Canada (nine), Ghana (eight), India (twenty), Kenya (four), Kuwait (two), Malaysia (fourteen), Muscat and Oman (three), Spain (sixteen), Tanzania (thirteen) and Zambia (five). In addition, the Royal Thai Police Force ordered three, and the Uganda Police Air Wing one. US Army Caribou, transferred on 1 January 1967 to the USAF, are designated CV-2A and C-7A, the latter having a higher all-up weight; those with the CAF are known as CC-108. The Caribou, which flew for the first time on 30 July 1958, is able to transport 32 armed troops or 26 paratroops. Other cargoes may include 2 loaded jeeps, 1 howitzer or 3 tons of freight. For casualty evacuation, the Caribou can take 22 stretchers and up to 8 other passengers, either sitting patients or medical attendants.

21 De Havilland Canada DHC-5 Buffalo

Despite its high-mounted tailplane, new engines and even more 'utility' appearance, the Buffalo is quite clearly a product of the same design thought which produced the Caribou STOL transport. Structurally, however, the Buffalo does not have a great deal in common with its stablemate, although it, too, is intended as a tactical support transport for combat areas. Its fuselage is much larger, enabling it to lift not only greater loads but a greater variety of loads than the Caribou. The US Army was envisaged as the largest potential customer, to whose May 1962 requirement the project was originated as the Caribou II. The cabin has accommodation for 41 troops or 35 paratroops, or for 24 stretchers and 6 sitting patients. Palletised loads weighing up to 7,500 lb (3,400 kg) can be air-dropped by the Buffalo, and typical performances include a 13,843 lb (6,279 kg) payload over 440 nautical miles (815 km) or a 4,000 lb (1,815 kg) load over 1,885 nautical miles (3,490 km). Propeller-driving free turbines, in place of the Caribou's piston engines, give both greater operational economy and quicker deployment in the field. The prototype Buffalo flew on 9 April 1964, and a year later the US Army began evaluation of this and three other prototypes which they designated YAC-2 (late YCV-7A and eventually C-8A). Two of these were assigned to operations in Vietnam late in 1965. Fifteen were completed as CC-115's, with more powerful T64 engines and a nose radome increasing overall length by 1 ft 8 in (0·51 m), for the CAF's Air Transport Command, to whom deliveries were made during 1967–68. During 1969–70 a total of twenty-four Buffalos were delivered to the Fórça Aérea Brasileira, and in mid-1971 delivery began of sixteen ordered by the Fuerza Aérea del Peru.

22 Fairchild C-123 Provider

The number of transport aeroplanes that have successfully been evolved from gliders is extremely small, yet one such aircraft still playing an important transport role is the Fairchild Provider. The designation XC-123 was applied to an aeroplane, then known as the Avitruc, developed by Chase Aircraft from its experimental wartime glider, the XCG-20, and flown for the first time under power on 14 October 1949. After five pre-production C-123B's had been completed in 1963, further development of the C-123 was undertaken by Fairchild, which was chosen to build three hundred C-123B Providers for the US Air Force. The first production example was flown on 1 September 1954, and the Provider entered US Air Force service in July 1955. Providers were also supplied to the air forces of Saudi Arabia (six), Thailand (four) and Venezuela (eighteen). The Provider's internal capacity is sufficient for 60 armed troops or a 24,000 lb (10,886 kg) freight load, and its squat landing gear and upswept rear fuselage are ideal for tail-ramp loading. In Vietnam, in particular, where more than fifty have been used by TAC's 315th Air Commando Group near Saigon, the Provider's STOL and rough-strip performances have made it a leading tactical airlift vehicle in the muddy, obstacle-strewn jungle airstrips which are its usual haunt. Another task which has befallen the Provider is the defoliation of jungle areas suspected of being Viet Cong hide-outs. A large tank amidships dispenses the defoliation liquid via spray nozzles under the wings and tail of the aircraft; operations are frequently carried out at night, with flares dropped from the Provider first to illuminate the target area. This hazardous but effective task is only one of many duties, ranging from artillery movements to the dropping of food and other essential supplies, which are carried out by the Provider. On 30 July 1962 Fairchild first flew the YC-123H, a converted version with CJ610 auxiliary jet engines and wider-track landing gear. This was followed during 1966–69 by the modification of one hundred and eighty-three Providers to a similar configuration, but with 2,850 lb (1,293 kg) st J85-GE-17 auxiliary turbo-jets instead of the less powerful CJ610s. These aircraft, used principally in Vietnam, are designated C-123K. Ten other Providers were redesignated C-123J when fitted with wingtip jet engines. The US Coast Guard uses a C-123B variant, the SC-123B, equipped with APS-42 search radar in an extended nose cone.

23 Hawker Siddeley 748 and Andover

Since the first flight, on 24 June 1960, of this medium-range passenger transport, it has made encouraging headway in sales to commercial operators in many parts of the world. To a lesser extent, it has also been adopted by military air arms as a personnel transport or crew trainer. Based on the civil 748 Series 2, the version in service with RAF Air Support Command is known as the Andover CC. Mk 2; two form part of The Queen's Flight, and four others have VIP interiors for use as general staff transports. The Royal Flight of the Royal Thai Air Force has one HS 748, six are operating with the Força Aérea Brasileira, three with the Ecuadorean Air Force and two with the Zambian Air Force Presidential Flight. Others were ordered by the governments of Argentina (one), Brunei (one), Germany (two) and Venezuela (one). After assembling four 748 Series 1's from components supplied from Great Britain, the Kanpur Division of Hindustan Aeronautics is building five military Series 1's and forty Series 2's for the Indian Air Force. The Royal Australian Air Force placed an order for ten aircraft in December 1965. Two of these are used as C. Mk 2 VIP or standard personnel transports, while the other eight are fitted out as T. Mk 2 flying classrooms for training RAAF navigators Two others were ordered by the Royal Australian Navy.

When the RAF began looking, in the latter 1950s, for a new short-to medium-range tactical transport, the British government stipulated that this need should be met by adapting the Hawker Siddeley 748. More powerful engines were necessary, because of the heavy military loads involved; their larger-diameter propellers entailed moving the engine nacelles some 18 in (46 cm) further out on the wing but, more important, reduced still further the ground clearance available on what was, and had to remain, a low-wing aeroplane. This problem was solved with room to spare, for another feature of the Andover C. Mk 1, as this version of the 748 is known, is its unique landing gear. This is adjustable over a 3 ft (0·91 m) range so that the Andover can raise or lower its fuselage floor to the level of the cargo being loaded or unloaded; by this means it can 'kneel' to bring the fuselage floor as little as 3 ft 9 in (1·14 m) from ground level. The Andover C.1 is longer than the standard 748, has a strengthened floor, an integral cargo door/loading ramp in the upswept rear end, more internal fuel and redesigned vertical tail surfaces. Internal capacity ranges from 44 troops to 30 paratroops, 18 stretchers (plus attendants), or a 13,500 lb (6,125 kg) freight load. The prototype, converted from a standard HS 748, flew for the first time on 21 December 1963, and was followed by the first of thirty-one production aircraft (XS594) on 9 July 1965. These began to be delivered later in the same year, eventually equipping No 46 Squadron and part of No 32 Squadron of RAF Air Support Command and No 84 Squadron in the Persian Gulf.

24 Transall C-160

The C-160 is a typical example of international collaboration between European powers to evolve an aeroplane that satisfies the air force requirements of the countries concerned. In this case they are France and Germany, who began to compare notes on a joint requirement in the late 1950s, when both were considering the matter of a tactical and strategic transport aircraft to replace the Nord Noratlas. The name Transall is derived from *Trans*porter *All*ianz, and design and production is shared between the two countries, with VFW-Fokker of Germany as overall production manager. The Tyne engines are built jointly by a four-nation consortium. Provision exists for installing auxiliary underwing jet engines if required. The first of three flying prototypes was flown on 25 February 1963, and the first of six pre-production C-160A's (three for each air force) in May 1965. Production orders have comprised one hundred and ten C-160D's for the Luftwaffe (first flight 2 November 1967), fifty C-160F's for the Armée de l'Air (first flight 13 April 1967), and nine C-160Z's (first flight 28 February 1969) for the South African Air Force. The first German and French units to equip with Transalls were, respectively, Lufttransportgeschwader 63 and the 61e Escadre de Transport; deliveries were continuing in 1972. The SAAF aircraft are operated by No 28 Squadron. In June 1971 the first of twelve C-160D's were supplied by Germany to the Turkish Air Force. The C-160 has a first-class short-field STOL performance, and an excellent carrying capacity. Typical tactical payload is 8 tonnes (which can be doubled over short ranges); alternatively, up to 93 troops, 81 paratroops or 62 casualty litters can be transported. The effective cargo volume of the

Transall's fuselage is nearly 5,000 cu ft. Although primarily for tactical or strategic transport missions, the C-160 could have other applications such as survey, weather reconnaissance or search and rescue.

25 Grumman C-2 Greyhound

To meet a US Navy requirement for a COD (Carrier On-board Delivery) supply transport, Grumman modified its basic E-2 Hawkeye design (which see) in similar fashion to its earlier adaptation of the S-2 Tracker into the C-1 Trader. The process consisted basically of mating the wings, powerplant and tail unit (without dihedral) of the E-2A with a new and enlarged fuselage, provided with a ramp and loading doors at the rear and capable of accommodating a variety of palletised or other cargo, up to a maximum of 10,000 lb (4,535 kg), 20 stretchers and 4 attendants, or up to 39 passengers. The first of two flying prototypes was flown on 18 November 1964, and delivery of an initial batch of seventeen C-2A Greyhounds was made during 1966–68, the first operator (December 1966) being Squadron VRC-50. A further eight C-2A's were ordered in the FY 1970 defence budget. The Greyhound carries a flight crew of 2, has similar all-weather capability to the Hawkeye, and can be catapulted from, and make arrested landings on, current types of US aircraft carrier.

26 Nord Noratlas

Employing the cargo pod and twin tailboom layout first proved on the Fairchild C-82 and C-119 and seen more recently in the Hawker Siddeley Argosy, the Noratlas has probably been used more extensively in Europe than any other short/medium-range tactical transport since the mid-1950s. It originated from the SNCA du Nord 2500 prototype (F-WFKL), first flown on 10 September 1949, although the true prototype, the Nord 2501 (F-WFRG), did not fly until 28 November 1950. This differed chiefly in having Bristol Hercules radial engines instead of its predecessor's SNECMA-built Gnome-Rhônes. Three N2501 pre-series aircraft were ordered for evaluation by the Armée de l'Air, the first of these making its first flight on 10 September 1952. Delivery of an initial batch of forty N2501's to the Armée de l'Air was completed on 25 June 1954, and follow-on orders eventually raised to some two hundred the total number of this version for the French Air Force. They served widely with units of COTAM (Commandement du Transport Aérien Militaire), and many were still in service at the beginning of the 1970s. The other major operator of the N2501 version has been the Federal German Luftwaffe, with whom it entered service in 1958. Twenty-five were assembled in Germany from French-built components, and a further one hundred and thirty-six were built in Germany by the Nordflug consortium; these bore the designation N2501D, the first flight by a German-built Noratlas taking place on 6 August 1958. Thirty N2501's were supplied to Israel, about a dozen to Portugal, and three ex-German Noratlases were sold to the Niger Air Force. The central fuselage pod, the doors of which are removable for air-dropping of loads, can accommodate 45 soldiers, 36 paratroops, 18 casualty litters, various artillery pieces and/or army vehicles, or about 7½ tons of freight.

A number of Noratlas variants were either projected or built in small numbers. The N2502 was a civil passenger transport, operated by UAT (seven) and Air Algérie (three); six of the UAT aircraft later went to the Portuguese Air Force. One N2503, converted from the prototype N2501, was flown with Pratt & Whitney R-2800-CB17 engines; the N2504 (five built, first flight 17 November 1958) was an anti-submarine warfare training version for France's Aéronavale; the N2506, first flown 20 August 1957, was a proposed assault version with slotted flaps, air brakes, telescopic main landing gear and low-pressure tyres, production plans for which were cancelled in a subsequent budget cutback; and the N2508, of which two were completed (one serving briefly with Kalinga Air Lines) with 2,500 hp R-2800-CB17 engines. These were allocated later as systems testbeds for the Franco-German Transall C-160 transport. All of these had auxiliary power in the form of a Turboméca Marboré jet engine mounted at each wingtip. The N2505, N2507, N2509 and N2510 were projected versions that were never built.

27 North American Rockwell OV-10 Bronco

Although employed predominantly by the US Air Force, the Bronco was the outcome of a LARA (Light Armed Reconnaissance Aircraft) design competition announced by the US Navy at the end of 1963. From a number of competing designs the North American NA-300 was selected in the following August, and a development contract followed for seven YOV-10A evaluation aircraft. The first of these was flown on 16 July 1965, each of the first four aircraft having a 30 ft 0 in (9·14 m) wing span and 600 shp T76–GE-6/8 engines. The seventh YOV-10A was fitted with Pratt & Whitney T74 turboprops, but it was the sixth aircraft which eventually set the standard for the initial production version by having uprated T76 engines, a 10 ft 0 in (3·05 m) increase in wing span, anhedral on the stub wings which provide four of the aircraft's seven external stores stations, and several other detail changes. There were changes also to the original specification, involving the installation of a self-sealing fuel system and armour protection for the 2-man crew, with the result that flight testing of the production configuration did not begin until March 1967, some 5 months after the placing of the initial production contracts. The first production OV-10A was flown on 6 August 1967. By April 1969 one hundred and fifty-two OV-10A's had been built for the USAF, ninety-six for the US Marine Corps and eighteen for the

US Navy. Production then ended, but was resumed later in the year to fulfil orders for six OV-10B's and twelve OV-10B(Z)'s for the Federal German government and sixteen OV-10C's for the Royal Thai Air Force. The first OV-10B was flown on 3 April 1970. The OV-10B(Z), which flew for the first time on 3 September 1970, differs in having a dorsally-mounted pod containing a 2,950 lb (1,338 kg) st General Electric J85-GE-4 turbojet engine to boost performance; all of the German aircraft were purchased for target-towing duties. The first OV-10C was flown on 9 December 1970. Deliveries of the OV-10A to the USAF and USMC began in February 1968, the first units to become operational with Broncos being the 19th Tactical Air Support Squadron (August 1968) and VMO-2 (July 1968) respectively, both in Vietnam. In combat, the Bronco has proved itself an able and versatile performer, pleasant to fly, easy to manoeuvre and capable of withstanding considerable battle damage. As already indicated, the OV-10A has two stub-wings sprouting from the lower fuselage; these have four built-in 0·30 in machine-guns, and four attachment points for a total of up to 2,400 lb (1,088 kg) of externally-mounted weapons. A fifth stores point on the fuselage centre-line can carry a 1,200 lb (544 kg) load, and provision exists for a 500 lb (227 kg) capacity station under each wing so long as a maximum weapons load of 3,600 lb (1,632 kg) is not exceeded. The stub-wings and armament capabil-ity are omitted from the OV-10B, though an auxiliary fuel tank can be carried on the centre-line station; the OV-10C is basically similar to the OV-10A but does not have the provision for underwing stores. Two night-flying 'gunship' aircraft, designated YOV-10D, were built for evaluation by the USMC, and a number of other OV-10A's were allocated for conversion under the USAF's Pave Nail programme for night forward air control and strike duties.

28 **Grumman OV-1 Mohawk**
When the first mock-up of the Mo-hawk (then known as the AO-1) was completed in 1957, the aircraft had a single fin and rudder with a high-mounted tailplane; the change to the present twin unit was one of several improvements made before the first Mohawk (57-6463, one of nine YAO-1AF test aircraft, later redesignated YOV-1A) was flown on 14 April 1959. The Mohawk's main function is to provide observa-tion and reconnaissance cover for the US Army, although it is fully capable of more active participation in land engagements. It can operate in all weathers, and from grass fields and short, unprepared emergency landing strips, thanks to an excellent STOL performance (it has been described as 'very hard to upset aerodynamically'); and the large forward-mounted cabin for the 2-man crew affords a generous field of vision in all directions. There are four basic models. The OV-1A (thirty-six built) has a 42 ft 0 in (12·80 m) wing span and is equipped

with standard-type aerial reconnaissance cameras; the OV-1B has
a 6 ft 0 in (1·83 m) greater wing
span and carries sideways-looking
airborne radar, for terrain mapping,
in a long, torpedo-like pod slung
beneath the lower starboard side of
the fuselage; the OV-1C is similar
to the OV-1A but with infra-red
surveillance equipment; and the
OV-1D, with the extended wings of
the OV-1B, is a version capable of
rapid interchange from infra-red to
SLAR capability, so fulfilling the
roles of both the B and C models.
The Mohawk entered service in
1962, and more than three hundred
and seventy-five were built before
production ended in December
1970. For offensive missions, the
Mohawk has four underwing attachment points on which napalm
or fragmentation bombs, anti-tank
weapons or auxiliary fuel tanks, up
to a maximum load of 3,740 lb
(1,696 kg), can be carried.

29 Grumman S-2 Tracker,
C-1 Trader and E-1 Tracer

The Tracker, in service the
US Navy since February 1954,
combined for the first time in one
aeroplane the dual roles of submarine hunter and killer, formerly
undertaken by two separate aircraft. Following the flight of the first
of two XS2F-1 prototypes (originally
called the Sentinel) on 4 December
1952, Grumman completed one
thousand one hundred and seventy-
seven Trackers, many for export,
and the type has also formed the
basis for the C-1 Trader transport
and the E-1 Tracer early warning

aircraft. De Havilland Canada
built a hundred Trackers (forty-
three CS2F-1 and fifty-seven
CS2F-2/-3), some of these also being
exported. The Grumman S-2A, of
which seven hundred and fifty-
three were built, was delivered to
the US Navy and was also supplied
to the Aviación Naval of Argentina
(six), the Japan Maritime Self
Defence Force (sixty), the Netherlands' Koninklijke Marine (twenty-
four, plus seventeen CS2F-1), the
Fôrça Aérea Brasileira (thirteen
CS2F-1), and the Aeronautica
Militare Italiano (forty-eight).
Other Trackers have been supplied
to Taiwan (nine), Thailand, Turkey (twelve) and Uruguay (three).
S-2B was the US Navy designation
of the S-2A when modified to carry
Jezebel and Julie acoustic search
and echo ranging equipment. Sixty
S-2C's were built with an extruded,
offset weapons bay: most of these
were later converted to US-2C and
RS-2C for utility and reconnaissance roles respectively. The
major US versions in current use
are the S-2D, which appeared in
1959, and the S-2E. The S-2D
featured a 1 ft 6 in (0·46 m) fuselage
extension, enlarged tail surfaces
and a 2 ft 11 in (0·89 m) increase in
wing span. Production of one
hundred and twenty-one S-2D's for
the USN was undertaken, the first
example making its maiden flight
on 21 May 1959. The S-2D's
equipment includes ECM gear in
wingtip housings, sonobuoys stowed
in the rear of the engine nacelles,
six underwing stores stations in
addition to the internal weapons

bay and a retractable MAD 'sting' in the tail. It has an endurance of about 9 hours and carries a 4-man crew. Production of the Tracker continued until 1968 with the S-2E, a development of the D having the Jezebel/Julie combination of location and attack systems. Two hundred and forty-one S-2E's were built, including fourteen ordered by the Royal Australian Navy as Gannet replacements. Altogether the US Navy operated at least eighteen S-2D/S-2E squadrons. The Canadian Trackers equipped squadrons VU 32, VU 33 and VS 880 of the Royal Canadian Navy, and the fourteen S-2E's of the Royal Australian Navy were delivered to No 816 Squadron.

In 1957 there entered service with the USN a transport derivative of the S-2D, the C-1A Trader. First flown in January 1955, this was an interim COD (Carrier On-board Delivery) transport pending delivery of the C-2A Greyhound (which see), and had a deeper, wider fuselage accommodating nine passengers or a 3,500 lb (1,587 kg) freight load. Eighty-seven production aircraft were built, equipping three Flight Logistics Support and Transport Squadrons of the US Navy. Four of these aircraft were modified to EC-1A for ECM duties.

Following the first flight on 1 March 1957 of an aerodynamic prototype, Grumman also built eighty-eight production examples of the E-1B Tracer, an airborne early warning aircraft for the USN, based upon the airframe of the

C-1A. This was distinguishable by its triple-fin-and-twin-rudder tail assembly and the huge oval dorsal fairing for its APS-82 search radar. Deliveries of E-1B's were made from 1958 to US Navy Squadrons VAW-11 and VAW-12, for deployment with various Carrier Air Wings pending the entry into service of the E-2A Hawkeye (which see) in the mid-1960s. Some Tracers were still in USN service in 1970.

30   Breguet Atlantic

The Atlantic, successor to the Neptune in the maritime patrol class for NATO air forces, represents the first true multi-nation aeroplane to gain service acceptance. Fourteen nations took part in its original planning, and the design was selected over two dozen others submitted. Three years later to the day, on 21 October 1961, the first prototype made its maiden flight. Entry of the Atlantic into squadron service was protracted, partly due to an inadequate number of prototypes being procured. Originally, only two were ordered; a third, 3 ft $3\frac{1}{4}$ in (1·00 m) longer, was completed to pre-production standard when prototype No 2 crashed during a test flight. This first flew on 25 February 1963, and was later joined by a second pre-production aircraft. These were followed by orders for forty for France's Aéronavale and twenty for the German Bundesmarine, the first for each service being delivered in December 1965. In mid-1968, nine Atlantics were ordered by the Royal Netherlands Navy, and the

Italian Navy subsequently ordered eighteen. The last four of the initial sixty, and five from the second production run, completed the Dutch order. Then follow those for Italy, and finally four others to complete the original French order. Dutch designation of the Atlantic is SP-13A. Final assembly of the Atlantic is undertaken by Breguet after component manufacture by firms in France, Belgium, Germany and the Netherlands. All four countries, and the United States, share production costs. The Atlantic's low-mid wing position, combined with a 'double-bubble' fuselage, leaves the upper half of the fuselage, which is pressurised, uncluttered by structural interference, and here the aircraft's 'operations room' is situated. The 29½ ft (9·00 m) weapons bay in the unpressurised lower fuselage can hold an impressive assortment of standard NATO stores – mines, depth charges, homing torpedoes, bombs, flares and sonobuoys – while there are two underwing points for air-to-surface missiles. The French CSF search radar is in the retractable 'dustbin' aft of the nosewheel bay; there is an MAD (magnetic anomaly detector) in the tail boom, and an ECM (electronic countermeasures) pod on top of the fin. A crew of 12 is carried normally, with provision for a full relief crew to be carried for extra-long missions. The Atlantic has a maximum endurance of 18 hours at 195 mph (320 km/hr) patrol speed.

31 Beriev Be-12 ('Mail')

Georgi Mikhailovich Beriev, with a lifetime's work on marine aircraft behind him, has been responsible since World War 2 for at least three noteworthy flying-boats for the Soviet Navy. Of these, the twin-engined Be-6 (NATO code name 'Madge') entered service in about 1949, some 2 years after the LL-143 prototype had made its first flight. Powered by two 2,300 hp Shvetsov ASh-73TK radial engines, the Be-6 had a wing span of 108 ft 3¾ in (33·00 m) and a length of 76 ft 1½ in (23·20 m). Normal gross weight was 51,588 lb (23,400 kg), and a maximum speed of 258 mph (415 km/hr) was attainable at 7,875 ft (2,400 m). For defensive armament, the Be-6 had a 23 mm gun in each of the dorsal and tail positions, and carried a variety of bombs, depth charges or other weapons on underwing pylons. It remained in fairly widespread use until the mid-1960s, but has since been superseded by later flying-boats or land-based aircraft.

In 1961 the Western nations obtained their first glimpse of the jet-powered Be-10 ('Mallow'), four of which took part in the fly-past at that year's Tushino Air Display. Powered by two 14,330 lb (6,500 kg) st Type AL-7PB turbojet engines mounted on the fuselage beneath the roots of its sweptback shoulder wings, the Be-10 had a span of 73 ft 2 in (22·30 m), length of 102 ft 0½ in (31·10 m) and normal gross weight of about 90,390 lb (41,000 kg); maximum speed was 565 mph (910 km/hr) at 4,925 ft

(1,500 m). Armament consisted of two 23 mm cannon in each of the nose and tail positions. The Be-10 is not thought to have served in very large numbers with the A-VMF (Soviet Naval Aviation), and has been replaced by the turboprop-powered Be-12 ('Mail').

In overall appearance the Be-12 bears a superficial resemblance to the earlier Be-6. However, the provision of turboprop power, a retractable wheeled landing gear to give amphibious capability, and the latest in sea-going detection equipment and anti-shipping weapons, clearly mark the Be-12 as one of the major maritime patrol aircraft currently in service. It was first seen at Tushino in 1961, at the same time as the Be-10, and in October 1964 the designation M-12 was quoted for an aircraft of the Be-12 type which set up six new international height records (with and without payload) for seaplanes. These revealed that the aircraft was capable of reaching 39,977 ft (12,185 m) without a payload, and of carrying a 22,046 lb (10,000 kg) load to an altitude of 30,682 ft (9,352 m). Closed-circuit speed and distance records followed during 1968, by which year production examples of the Be-12 were in service with the Northern and Black Sea Fleets of the Soviet Navy. More recently, they have been reported in operation from Egyptian bases. Externally visible features of the Be-12 include an elongated 'thimble' radome on the nose, a retractable MAD (magnetic anomaly detection) 'sting' housed in the extreme

rear of the fuselage, an internal weapons bay aft of the hull step and three pylons beneath each wing for the carriage of external stores.

32 Grumman E-2 Hawkeye

The name of Fennimore Cooper's famous American hero is an apt choice for the Grumman E-2, even though the airborne Hawkeye does not carry a single gun. The E-2 is the lynch-pin of the US Navy's Airborne Tactical Data System, serving with VAW-11 in the Pacific and VAW-12 in the Atlantic. Hawkeyes operate in teams of two or more aircraft, flying at altitudes in the region of 30,000 ft (9,145 m) to provide long-range early warning of potential threats from hostile surface vessels and fast-flying aircraft. The key to this system is the powerful AN/APA-143 search radar, carried in the 24 ft (7·32 m) diameter radome on the Hawkeye's back, which rotates once every ten seconds while the aircraft is in flight. In addition, the substantial fuselage contains detection and digital computers, data link systems and other complex electronics which account for nearly a quarter of the aircraft's total weight. The Hawkeye's radome can be lowered 2 ft (0·61 m) to facilitate stowage aboard the parent carrier. Three systems operators are carried, together with 2 pilots, in the pressurised cabin. Originally designated W2F-1, an aerodynamic prototype flew for the first time on 21 October 1960; a fully-equipped prototype followed on 19 April 1961. The US Navy began to receive the initial production version, the E-2A, in January 1964, and fifty-nine of this model were eventually completed, the last being delivered in the spring of 1967. In the same year first details were announced of the E-2B, with enlarged outer fins, improved avionics, provision for in-flight refuelling and other modifications. All E-2A's were brought up to this standard, beginning in 1969, the first flight by an E-2B taking place on 20 February 1969. The latest version so far announced is the E-2C, a prototype of which flew for the first time on 20 January 1971. Production began in the following summer, and this version is due to enter US Navy service in 1973, working in conjunction with the E-2B force. It differs from the E-2B primarily in having AN/APS-111, an advanced radar capable of detecting airborne targets in a 'land-clutter' environment. The initial order is for eleven aircraft. A transport derivative of the Hawkeye, the C-2 Greyhound, is described separately.

33 Lockheed P-2 Neptune

A continuous production/service record of more than 25 years, at the end of which it was still giving excellent service to the US Navy as well as the air arms of seven other countries, is a measure of the place the Neptune has held in the field of patrol aircraft since the end of World War 2. The first steps towards its design were taken before Pearl Harbor, although the prototype XP2V-1 did not fly until 17 May 1945 and the Neptune did not enter USN service until 1947-48.

Intended basically for anti-shipping and submarine patrol, the Neptune has also fulfilled such secondary roles as torpedo attack, minelaying and reconnaissance. The early P-2A to D (originally P2V-1 to -4), no longer in service, accounted for two hundred and thirty-three aircraft (including two prototypes); they were replaced by the P-2E, P-2F and P-2H versions. The P-2E (originally P2V-5, first flown on 29 December 1950), during its absorption into service, gradually introduced such features as a redesigned glazed nose, an MAD 'sting' in the tail, and modern anti-submarine gear such as the Jezebel/Julie system. The P-2F, first flown on 16 October 1952, introduced a further-modified nose, smaller tip-tanks, a ventral radome and wider load-carrying capabilities. The P-2H (originally P2V-7, first flight 26 April 1954) offered further equipment and detail changes, and had additional power from two pod-mounted jet engines beneath the wings; this last feature was retrospectively applied to all P-2E's in service, and also to some P-2F's which, with this feature, were redesignated P-2G. The largest Neptune operator outside the United States was France's Aéronavale, which had six squadrons of P-2E/F/H. Neptunes also served with the RCAF (one squadron of twenty-five P-2H); the Koninklijke Marine (four squadrons of P-2E/H); the Fôrça Aérea Portuguesa (one squadron of twelve ex-Dutch P-2E); the RAAF (one squadron of twelve P-2H); the Japan Maritime

Self Defence Force (five squadrons of P-2H – seventy-six aircraft, of which forty-eight were licence-built in Japan by Kawasaki); Argentina's Aviación Naval (one squadron of six P-2E); and the Fôrça Aérea Brasileira (one squadron of fourteen P-2E). Two missile-carrying variants of the Neptune were the MP-2F of the US Navy, armed with the Petrel anti-submarine weapon, and the Dutch P-2H's, carrying the Nord AS.12. Overall US production amounted to one thousand and ninety-nine aircraft, including four hundred and twenty-four P-2E's, eighty-three P-2F's and three hundred and fifty-nine P-2H's. Argentina, Australia, Brazil, France, Japan, the Netherlands and Portugal continued to operate Neptunes in 1971.

To replace its P-2H/P2V-7 Neptunes in the 1970s, the Japan MSDF began to receive in February 1971 an improved version of the aircraft designated P-2J. This was developed by Kawasaki from the P2V-7, from which it differs structurally in having a 4 ft 2 in (1·27 m) longer fuselage, redesigned main landing gear and additional rudder area. Licence-built General Electric turboprops replace the original piston engines, and the auxiliary underwing turbojets are of Japanese design. Operational equipment is of a comparable standard to that carried by the Lockheed P-3 Orion, and includes APS-80J search radar in the ventral fairing. An aerodynamic prototype of the P-2J was flown on 21 July 1966, and the first production example on 8 August 1969. Forty-six were to be built according to plans announced up the end of 1971.

34 Lockheed P-3 Orion

When it became necessary to find a successor to the long-lived Neptune for the maritime patrol squadrons of the US Navy, Lockheed decided to base its entry in the official design competition on its commercial turboprop airliner, the Electra. This entry won the competition and, as the P-3A Orion, entered squadron service in August 1962. As compared with the Electra, the Orion's forward fuselage, which includes the internal weapons bay, is some 7 ft (2·13 m) shorter; and it has the familiar MAD 'sting' projecting beyond the tail. The wing and tail surfaces are standard Electra components. Inside the Orion's fully-pressurised fuselage are some $2\frac{1}{2}$ tons of electronics equipment, and accommodation for a crew of 10 on patrols of up to 18 hours. The internal ordnance load may be up to 7,252 lb (3,290 kg), comprising three or four homing torpedoes with nuclear or high explosive warheads, nuclear depth charges, sea mines or other maritime stores. In addition the Orion has ten underwing attachment points for external stores. One of these is normally occupied by a searchlight, but the remaining nine may be utilised for additional mines or torpedoes, rocket pods or Zuni rocket launchers. Initial flight testing was conducted with a modified Electra airframe, first flown on 19 August 1958, followed by a YP3V-1 operational prototype on 25 November 1959. The US Navy ordered a total of two hundred and eighty-six of two basic production models, the P-3A and P-3B. Of these, more than one hundred were P-3A's, those from the 110th aircraft onwards having more sensitive detection equipment and being known as Deltic P-3A's. First flight by a production P-3A was made on 15 April 1961, and the first operational Orion units were VP-8 and VP-44. A weather reconnaissance version, the WP-3A, was delivered in small numbers in 1970. The P-3B is basically similar to the P-3A except for higher-powered Allison T56 engines, and this version has also been delivered to the air forces of Australia (ten), New Zealand (five) and Norway (five). Electronics reconnaissance versions for the US Navy are designated EP-3E (ten converted from P-3A's and two others from previously-converted EP-3B's). The latest basic version of the Orion is the P-3C, first flown on 18 September 1968. This entered service in the following year and has considerably more advanced computer-based detection and control equipment.

35 **Canadair CP-107 Argus**
For many years after the end of World War 2, ocean-going patrol missions for the Royal Canadian Air Force were carried out by modified versions of the Lancaster bomber. By the early 1950s, however, the RCAF began looking for a successor able to cope with the more demanding requirements of maritime patrol, and one which could combine the 'hunter' and 'killer' aspects of submarine detection. The aeroplane chosen, the Argus, was the result of much close study and co-operation between Canadair and the Bristol company, builders of the Britannia airliner. The Argus employs the same wing, tail, undercarriage and flight control systems as the airliner, with engines of US manufacture and a completely new fuselage of Canadian design. The Wright Turbo-Compound engines were more economical than turboprops for prolonged low-altitude patrol work, and an unpressurised fuselage was also considered adequate. Equipment in the Argus includes search radar in the bulge under the 'chin', a movable searchlight on the starboard wing, and MAD (magnetic anomaly detection) gear in the tail 'sting'. Two 18 ft 6 in (5·64 m) internal weapons bays each hold up to 4,000 lb (1,815 kg) of mines, depth charges, homing torpedoes, bombs or other stores, and a further 3,800 lb (1,725 kg) can be carried on each of two underwing stations. The usual number of crew is 15. The Argus was first flown on 28 March 1957, and production ended in July 1960 after thirteen Mk 1 (with US search radar) and twenty Mk 2 (British radar, in a smaller fairing) had been built. The Argus entered service in 1958, and currently serves with 404, 405, 407 and 415 Squadrons of the Canadian Armed Forces, with whom it is scheduled to continue in operation until 1973.

36 Shin Meiwa PS-1

Due to enter service with the Japan Maritime Self Defence Force in 1972–73, the PS-1 anti-submarine flying-boat has a development history going back to 1959, when Shin Meiwa (successor to the former Kawanishi Aircraft Company) completed the rebuilding of a Grumman UF-1 Albatross amphibian as a small-scale flying model of the new design. Flight testing of this aircraft, which was known as the UF-XS, ended in September 1964, and in January 1966 the Japan Defence Agency awarded Shin Meiwa a development contract and an order for two prototype aircraft designated PX-S. Designed under the leadership of Dr Shizuo Kikuhara, the first PX-S was completed in August 1967 and flew for the first time on 5 October that year. This aircraft bore the serial number 5801; the second aircraft (5802) made its first flight on 14 June 1968, and by the end of 1968 both had begun evaluation by the 415th Flight Test Squadron of the JMSDF at Iwakuni. Two more aircraft, ordered in March 1969, were due for delivery by the spring of 1972, and are pre-production models with the JMSDF designation PS-1. Production plans up to spring 1972 were for the delivery of ten more PS-1's by March 1974 and purchase of another twenty by 1976.

As one of the only two modern maritime reconnaissance flying-boats in production/service, the Japanese design is of particular interest. It possesses an excellent STOL performance which includes a touchdown speed of only 47 mph (76 km/hr) and a take-off run of less than 1,000 ft (305 m) to clear a 50 ft (15 m) obstacle. Its anti-submarine equipment includes Jezebel acoustic search gear and twenty sonobuoys, Julie echo ranging gear with thirty explosive charges, smoke bombs, four 330 lb (150 kg) anti-submarine bombs, search radar in the nose, and a retractable MAD probe in the rear of the fuselage. Four homing torpedoes and six 5 in (12·7 cm) air-to-surface rockets can be carried beneath the wings, and a searchlight is installed below the outer starboard wing panel. The PS-1 is able to operate in rough seas with waves of 13 ft (4 m) or higher, and in winds of up to 25 knots (47 km/hr), using its 'dunking' sonar while at rest on the surface, and has a patrol endurance of 15 hours. A crew of 10 is normally carried. High-lift devices are fitted, and low-speed stability and control are aided by a boundary layer control system which 'blows' the flaps, elevators and rudder. Carefully-positioned bow grooves and strakes and a high angle of wing incidence keep the engines and propellers well clear of spray, and a retractable tricycle beaching gear is built into the hull. The wingtip floats are non-retractable.

A second version, the air/sea rescue SS-2A (manufacturer's designation of the PS-1 being SS-2), was announced during 1970. This would be basically similar to the PS-1, retaining the nose radar but carrying five medical attendants and up to 18 stretchers, or up to 69 passengers in an all-transport role. Wing span would be slightly reduced, and a retractable tricycle landing gear fitted. Other variants under consideration include an early-warning patrol version, and amphibious and landplane commercial transport versions.

37 Lockheed C-121 Super Constellation

This veteran aeroplane dates from the Model 049 Constellation airliner, which had no time to establish itself in the commercial market before the USA's entry into World War 2, when fifteen were delivered as C-69 military transports. After the war the Constellation achieved a deserved success with the world's airlines, and ten aircraft of the Model L-749 type were completed as long range personnel carriers for the US Air Force. One of these was equipped as a VC-121B with VIP interior, and the remainder as PC-121A standard transports. A stretch of the Constellation resulted in the Model L-1049 Super Constellation with a much increased seating capacity in its 18 ft 4 in (5·59 m) longer fuselage, and the service equivalents of this model included four C-121A VIP transports, thirty-three C-121C's for the USAF and thirty-two R7V-1's for the Navy. Capacity of the C-121C (and the generally similar R7V-1, some of which became C-121G on transfer to MAC) is 106 passengers, or 72 passengers plus 47 casualty litters with their attendants, or a 40,000 lb (18,144 kg) cargo payload. In addition to the transport variants, there are numerous radar or ECM picket and AEW versions with Air Force or Navy formations, serving under such designations as RC-121C (for AEW duties; ten built, later redesignated EC-121C); RC-121D (seventy built, some later to EC-121H); C121J (ex-R7V-1); EC-121K (ex-WV-2); EC-121L (ex-WV-2E); EC-121M (ex-WV-2Q); WC-121N (for weather reconnaissance; ex-WV-3); and EC-121P (ex-WV-2). The picket versions, distinguished by a large ventral 'guppy' radome and a second fairing, resembling a submarine conning tower, above the fuselage, carry crews of up to 31 men. Other variants have included the EC-121D and H (airborne fighter control) and C-121J (airborne communications relay stations). The Indian Air Force operates eight Super Constellations for search and rescue, and one as a transport.

38 Hawker Siddeley Argosy

It took the British aircraft industry nearly twenty years to follow its American colleagues by putting into service a general purpose transport aeroplane with a pod-and-tailboom configuration. The Fairchild C-82 paved the way, followed by the larger C-119 and then the French Noratlas; the fourth, and possibly the last, to follow this layout is the Hawker Siddeley Argosy, which was produced in both civil and military forms. The latter, designed to meet an Air Ministry requirement for a Hastings replacement for RAF

Transport Command, differs from its commercial counterpart in having 'beaver-tail' vertically-opening doors at the rear of the cargo pod, and a non-opening nose, at the forward extremity of which is a 'thimble' fairing containing a weather radar. It also features strengthened wings and higher-powered Dart engines than the civil Argosy 650. The first military A.W.660 (XN814) flew on 4 March 1961, just over two years after the first civil prototype. Fifty-six Argosy C. Mk 1's, which began to enter service in March 1962, equipped two Transport Command (now Air Support Command) squadrons (Nos 114 and 267) and an OCU (No 242) at home, and one squadron each (Nos 70, 105 and 215) in the Near, Middle and Far East. Their personnel capacity includes sixty-nine troops, fifty-four paratroops or forty-eight stretchers with four attendants. Maximum short-range cargo payload (29,000 lb; 13,154 kg) includes individual pieces of up to 8,500 lb (3,855 kg) in weight, and typical Army loads may be a Ferret scout car or Wombat anti-tank gun. A standard medium range tactical transport, until it was withdrawn from transport service during 1971, the Argosy appeared during its later service life in two-tone camouflage with black undersurfaces, similar to that shown in the Hercules and Andover illustrations in this edition. In 1971 some remained in service with No 115 Squadron for radar and navigation calibration duties, with the new designation E. Mk 1. Some others are to be used as advanced navigation and electronics trainers.

39 Canadair CC-106 Yukon

Like the Argus, the Yukon is also descended from the Bristol Britannia airliner, although it has a considerably longer fuselage. It was developed by Canadair as a civil and military transport, accent in the civil field being mainly on the CL-44D4 cargo version, whose entire tail section can be swung to one side to permit direct loading of freight into the fuselage hold. The military transport version was also used chiefly as a freighter, but instead of the swing-tail arrangement has more conventional side-loading facilities through two large cargo doors on the port side. The Yukon's internal capacity, including underfloor holds, is 7,391 cu ft (209·3 cu m), permitting payloads of 60,000 lb (27,215 kg) or more to be carried. Since its work is not confined to low levels like the Argus, the Yukon is pressurised, and follows the Britannia practice of using turboprop engines; it was in fact the first propeller-turbine aeroplane to go into production in Canada. First flight of a CC-106 (CL-44-6) was made on 15 November 1959, and a total of twelve aircraft was built. Two of these served as passenger transports (convertible to VIP use) with Air Transport Command's No 412 Squadron, and the remaining ten, with No 437 Squadron, Canadian Armed Forces, provided long-range logistics transport facilities for Canadian forces in Europe, Africa and the Middle East. The

Yukon was retired from CAF service in 1971; some aircraft had been sold to Argentina by the end of the year.

and were still being operated at the end of 1971. At that time no production orders had been placed.

40 Breguet 941S

Designed to lift cargo or passengers out of small airfields or from short unprepared strips, and carry them over ranges up to 1,925 miles (3,100 km), the Breguet 941 is potentially one of the most promising STOL transport aeroplanes yet to fly. Its capacious square-section fuselage, which is unpressurised, can hold up to 40 fully-equipped troops, 24 stretchers or a wide assortment of army vehicles and equipment. Human or other loads may be air-dropped via the extreme rear of the aircraft, after removing a door beneath the tailplane; and the rear fuselage floor lets down to become a ramp for ground loading. The aeroplane's STOL ability is achieved by the deflected slipstream technique. The 13 ft 8½ in (4·50 m) diameter propellers of its four shaft-turbine engines sweep almost the whole of the wing leading edges, and their slipstream acts in conjunction with an extensive system of flaps along the trailing edges to provide a high degree of lift. A gear linkage ensures that all propellers keep turning if an engine fails. A prototype ordered by the French government first flew on 1 June 1961, and in 1965 a batch of four evaluation Breguet 941S aircraft was put in hand for the Armée de l'Air. These have a later and more powerful version of the Turmo IIID engines which powered the first prototype,

41 Lockheed C-130 Hercules

Since it first entered service in December 1965, Lockheed's versatile and ubiquitous C-130 transport has far exceeded the twelve labours of its Grecian namesake. This middle-sized tactical haulier, which, say its pilots, is 'built like a truck and handles like a Cadillac', has been built in a score of variants, serves with as many countries, and fulfils a range of duties far beyond those of its original specification. More than twelve hundred Hercules had been ordered by the start of 1972, with production continuing. Within the same basic airframe, the payload and performance of the Hercules have increased steadily since the first of the two YC-130 prototypes made its maiden flight on 23 August 1954.

Initial production included two hundred and thirty-one C-130A's (first flight 7 April 1955), sixteen RC-130A's for aerial survey and two hundred and thirty C-130B's with higher-powered engines and extra fuel. Included in these figures were ten or eleven air-snatch JC-130A's, twelve ski-fitted C-130D's (converted from A's for USAF Polar supply duties), seven C-130F's (converted from B's for the US Navy), forty-six KC-130F assault transports/refuelling tankers for the US Marine Corps, four Navy LC-130F/R's on skis, for Polar supply, and twelve search and rescue HC-130G's, also converted from B's.

The major production version, for the US forces and for export, has been the C-130E, of which the first example was flown on 25 August 1961. This is essentially an extended-range version of the C-130B, with underwing auxiliary fuel tanks; it entered service in April 1962, and five hundred and ten had been ordered up to late 1971. Apart from those for the US forces, Hercules have been ordered by the air arms of Argentina (five C-130E), Australia (twelve C-130E), Belgium (twelve C-130H), Brazil (eleven C-130E), Canada (twenty-four C-130E), Colombia (two C-130E), Indonesia (eight C-130B), Iran (fifty-eight C-130E and twelve C-130H), Israel (C-130E), Italy (fourteen C-130H), Libya (six C-130E), Norway (six C-130H), Pakistan (eight C-130B and one C-130E), Peru (six C-130E), Saudi Arabia (nine C-130E), South Africa (seven C-130B), Spain (six C-130 and two KC-130), Sweden (two C-130E), Turkey (five C-130E), Venezuela (four C-130H) and Zaire (two C-130H). The C-130H has more powerful engines than the C-130E, but is otherwise generally similar. Accommodation is for a crew of 4 and up to 92 troops, 64 paratroops, 74 casualty litters and 2 attendants, or a maximum freight payload of 45,000 lb (20, 410 kg). Conversions of the C-130E include the close-support AC-130E (seven built), electronics reconnaissance EC-130E and weather reconnaissance WC-130E.

Later variants have included the USAF Aerospace Rescue and Recovery Service's HC-130H (sixty-three built, plus three others for the US Coast Guard) which has 'scissors' type nose-mounted pick-up gear; the C-130K (sixty-six as Hercules C. Mk 1 for RAF Air Support Command); the HC-130N search and rescue version (fifteen for the USAF); and the LC-130R for the US Navy. Twenty of the HC-130H's were later modified as HC-130P's to provide in-flight refuelling for helicopters.

42 Antonov An-12 ('Cub')

Featuring the high-mounted wing, with marked anhedral, that today characterises the whole range of Antonov's turbine transports from the An-24 to the gargantuan An-22, the medium-sized An-12 is a freighter development of the commercial An-10A described in the *Airliners since 1946* volume. Both aircraft derived from Antonov's earlier An-8, a smaller twin-engined design which did not achieve widespread service. The chief differences between the An-10A and An-12 lie in the latter's rear fuselage and tail assembly, which have been redesigned completely with modified vertical tail surfaces and a more upswept rear end incorporating an integral access door which is lowered to act as a loading ramp when the aircraft is on the ground. The An-12 is also rare among contemporary military transport aircraft in having provision for a defensive armament, this taking the form of a turret in the extreme tail capable of mounting a pair of 20 mm guns. It has been the standard medium-range trooper/freighter of Soviet A-VDV units since the early 1960s. Thirty-two were supplied to the Indian Air Force; the Angkatan Udara Republik Indonesia has about ten; the Algerian Air Force about eight; and others have been supplied to Egypt (about twenty) and Iraq (about eight) and Poland. The hold of the aircraft can accommodate most Soviet Army vehicles or artillery pieces, or a 'Guideline' missile and its supporting equipment. The crew consists of 5 men. A civil version of the An-12, with the tail gun position faired in, is in service in the USSR and some Soviet bloc countries as a freight transport. Combined military and civil production of the An-12 was reported to have exceeded nine hundred by 1971.

43 Short Belfast
On 20 January 1966 the airlift potential of the RAF's key strategic transport base at Brize Norton, Oxfordshire, took a step nearer realisation with delivery of the first Short Belfast C. Mk 1 to No 53 Squadron. This huge aeroplane, ten of which were built, complements the VC10's of No 10 squadron at the same base. The Belfast's lower deck can seat 150 troops, and up to 100 more can be accommodated by installing a removable upper floor; but operationally the VC10 is normally employed for all trooping activities, leaving the Belfast to handle freight movements, for which it was principally intended. Its capacious fuselage can hold a Blue Streak missile or a Chieftain tank, three Saladin armoured cars, Blood-hound missiles or Wessex helicopters, or ten Land-Rovers, as well as many other possible loads. Although intended mainly for strategic transportation, the Belfast can carry out tactical airlifts as well, having a range of 1,000 miles (1,610 km) with its maximum payload of 78,000 lb (35,400 kg), about double the load of the American Hercules. In this configuration the aircraft's all-up weight is just over a hundred tons. Design work leading to the Belfast began in the middle 1950s as a project for a Britannia development, and the proposal put forward by Short Bros, from which the SC. 5/10 Belfast was evolved, was originally named Britannic. The RAF order for the Belfast was placed in 1960, and the maiden flight of the first aircraft (XR362) took place on 5 January 1964. Since their entry into service the RAF Belfasts have been the subject of a modification programme, still continuing in 1971, which includes the installation of a fully-automatic triplex blind-landing system – the first, and so far the only, application of such a system to an operational military transport aircraft anywhere in the world.

44 Douglas C-133 Cargomaster
The Cargomaster, easily the largest American transport in service prior to the arrival of the Lockheed Star-Lifter, was built in comparatively modest numbers to provide a small but select force of large logistic transport aircraft for the Military Air

Transport Service (now called Military Airlift Command). The original production order was placed in 1954, and the first of thirty-five C-133A Cargomasters made its maiden flight on 23 April 1956; deliveries to the US Air Force began in October 1957. With a huge cylindrical, pressurised fuselage capable of transporting an Atlas, Thor or Jupiter missile, the C-133A has an integral loading ramp in the rear fuselage underside, and side-loading doors in the forward fuselage for alternative cargo loads. Its 90 ft (27·43 m) long, 13,000 cu ft (368 cu m) hold can accept 96 per cent of all US Army field force vehicles or equipment. Production of the Cargomaster came to an end in April 1961 after the construction of fifteen C-133B's, an improved version with uprated engines, a five-ton greater capacity, and clamshell rear doors which added 3 ft (0·91 m) to the usable length of the cargo hold. Capacity of the C-133B is more than 110,000 lb (49,900 kg) of freight or 200 fully-equipped troops; a 4-man crew is usual, although on especially long hauls a relief crew may also be carried. A series of accidents resulted in the grounding of the Cargomaster force early in 1965, but by May all the C-133B's and about two-thirds of the C-133A's were back in service. Phasing out of those remaining in service began in 1971.

45 Antonov An-22 ('Cock')

Just as, in 1959, the Soviet Union stole the show at the 23rd Salon de l'Aéronautique by flying in, un-announced, the world's largest airliner (the Tu-114), so in May 1965 it repeated the treatment by presenting what was then the world's largest aeroplane in any category, the enormous An-22. Flown into Le Bourget by Yuri Kourlin, the prototype (CCCP-46191), which had begun flight testing on 27 February 1965, had completed the Moscow–Paris journey in 5 hours 5 minutes. Although displayed then and later in Aeroflot markings, it has since become apparent that the An-22 is primarily a military logistics transport in the same category as the Lockheed C-5A Galaxy, to move missile batteries and large vehicles or equipment loads to and from areas lacking major airfield facilities. The main cargo hold is 14 ft 5 in (4·40 m) square and 108 ft 3 in (33·00 m) long, enabling it to lift nearly four times as much as the RAF's Belfast and permitting the carriage of a maximum payload that is not far short of the *basic empty weight* of the Tu-114. Although the production of an aeroplane of this size represents a considerable feat of engineering, the wings and fuselage of the An-22 are, fundamentally, no more than scaled-up counterparts of those on Antonov's smaller transports, the An-10 and An-12. The thin, high aspect ratio wings have double-slotted trailing-edge flaps, and the outer panels have Antonov's anhedral 'trademark'. A large rear-loading ramp/door permits the straightforward loading of cargo, large unpalletised items being hoisted on board by four overhead gantries. The bulky fairings amidships, besides housing the six-wheel main undercarriage bogies, contain the auxiliary power unit (starboard) and the crew doors (port and starboard) a navigation radar is located in the nose radome, and a larger second radome is positioned below and just aft of the nose windows. The An-22 probably entered Soviet Air Force service in 1967, when three military examples were included in the July Aviation Day display; four An-22's were used to carry relief supplies to Peru in 1970, after the earthquake disaster in that country, and the type is also in service with Aeroflot.

46 Tupolev Tu-95 ('Bear')

First revealed to Western observers at Tushino in July 1955, the Tu-95 is the world's first, last and only long-range strategic bomber with propeller-turbine engines, and (save for its civil transport counterpart, the Tu-114) the only large turboprop aeroplane to have sweptback wings. It is comparable in size with America's B-52, and its range is prodigious: Tu-95's regularly patrol both the Atlantic and Pacific oceans, and an unrefuelled range of 7,800 miles (12,550 km) has been quoted by official US sources. Many assessments of the total Tu-95 production have been made, the most likely being between two and three hundred. Of these, about eighty were estimated to remain in service at the end of 1965 with Russia's long-range strike force, the Dalnaya Aviatsiya. Most of them had by then been converted from their original Bear-A configuration, capable of carrying a 25,000 lb (11,340 kg) bomb load, to Bear-B, modifications including the physical changes necessary to carry modern air-launched weapons such as the 'Kangaroo' stand-off bomb under the belly, the provision of an enormous search and guidance radar in the lower nose, facilities for inflight refuelling, and a dorsal gun which is believed to fire decoy material to confuse opposing radar. The Bear-B version was first displayed publicly in 1961. The Tu-95 is employed today principally by naval aviation units of the A-VMF, in Bear-C and Bear-D versions for maritime reconnaissance, possibly with all or part of the weapons bay given over to additional fuel tankage. Bear-C has large blister fairings on both sides of the rear fuselage, while Bear-D has a 'chin' radome similar in shape to that of the Canadair Argus. Another variant is the Tu-114D, in service in small numbers as a cargo or airborne command-post aircraft; despite its designation, this is a straightforward conversion utilising a Tu-95 fuselage, and not the large fuselage and low wing arrangement of the commercial airliner. The large fuselage of the Tu-114 is, however, retained in a variant code-named 'Moss' by NATO. This is an airborne warning and control version, with modified tail surfaces (including a ventral fin), a huge saucer-shaped radome mounted on a pylon above the rear of the fuselage, and several blister fairings along the underside of the fuselage.

47 Lockheed U-2

There was a story that CIA, officially the initials of the US Central Intelligence Agency, stood also for 'Caught In the Act'; and certainly no aeroplane in history earned the latter description with such world-shaking effect as the U-2 in which Gary Powers was shot down over the Soviet Union on 1 May 1960. Whether or not the U-2 design was actually sponsored by the CIA, there is no doubt that prior to this time it was working on its cloak-and-dagger reconnaissance missions, for all its 'utility' category designation and its official description as a high altitude research aeroplane. Ironically, since the Powers affair, the USAF's U-2's have been obliged to perform just such duties, although the aircraft's contribution to aviation knowledge should not be minimised on that account. It did this work principally for the National Aeronautics and Space Administration, and with the 4028th and 4080th Strategic Reconnaissance Squadrons (Weather) of Strategic Air Command in the USA. The U-2 was flown for the first time in August 1955, and before its exposure as a spy-plane had flown from bases as far apart as Alaska, Pakistan, Japan, Nationalist China, Germany and the United Kingdom; and there was evidence as late as 1965 that Chinese Nationalist pilots were still being trained in the USA to fly the U-2. Production of the U-2 comprised forty-eight U-2A's and U-2B's, and five U-2D's. The U-2A has a J57 jet engine with auxiliary fuel in pinion tanks, and is a single-seater like the U-2B, which has the more powerful 17,000 lb (7,711 kg) st J75 engine. The U-2D is a 2-seat version of the B. Most of the U-2A's – about thirty are thought to have been built – were later brought up to U-2B standard. The remainder, for their weather reconnaissance role, were redesignated WU-2A. Among the U-2's tasks in more recent years have been the High Altitude Sampling Programme of upper atmosphere research on behalf of the Defense Atomic Support Agency, and the use of two aircraft by NASA in 1971–72 in connection with the launch of ERTS-A, the first Earth Resources Technology Satellite. It was reported early in 1972 that the U-2 might be reinstated in production for use as an unmanned target drone.

48 Lockheed SR-71

The SR-71, with its impressive if unorthodox appearance, began to be conceived in 1959, under the Lockheed designation A-11, not long before the Powers affair exploded the 'research aircraft' myth of the same company's U-2, and may be assumed to have been evolved originally for a similar purpose – with the important difference that it is built to perform its duties at Mach 3·5. So far about twenty-six are believed to have been built. The original three A-11's were converted during 1964 as YF-12A prototypes, for evaluation under the US Defense Department's IMI (Improved Manned Intercepter) programme; two of these were responsible in

1965 for several world-class performance records, including the first over-2,000 mph absolute speed record, which was still unbeaten in the spring of 1972. In addition to its high altitude capability, the YF-12A was designed to carry four Hughes Falcon interception missiles in each of the fairings flanking the long forward fuselage. About twenty-two A-11's were completed as SR-71A strategic reconnaissance aircraft, having a longer and somewhat cleaner fuselage without the ventral fins of the YF-12A. Both versions are 2-seaters, the accommodation being in tandem under individual cockpit hoods. The first A-11 flew towards the end of 1961, the first SR-71A on 22 December 1964. Strategic Air Command, which began to evaluate the SR-71A in the spring of 1965, has stated that the aircraft has daily exceeded the YF-12A speed record on test, and can cross the USA coast to coast in under an hour. The first and, to date, only SR-71A unit is the 4200th (now 9th) Strategic Reconnaissance Wing at Beale AFB, which began to receive the 'Blackbird' in January 1966. One SR-71B pilot trainer, with reinstated ventral fins and a raised rear cockpit, was delivered at about the same time. This aircraft was subsequently destroyed in a crash, but was replaced by one of the three YF-12A's, suitably converted and redesignated SR-71C.

49 Hawker Siddeley Buccaneer

No separate prototype was ordered of this 2-seat, low-level strike aeroplane, the initial contract, placed in July 1955, being for twenty B.103 development aircraft to meet Royal Navy requirement N.A.39. The first of these (XK486) was flown on 30 April 1958. After carrier trials on board HMS *Victorious*, the first Buccaneer S. Mk 1's were delivered to the Royal Navy in 1961, and the first squadron was commissioned in July 1962. Production of the 7,100 lb (3,220 kg) st Gyron Junior-engined S.1 totalled forty, these equipping Nos 800, 801 and 809 Squadrons and No 736 Training Squadron of the Fleet Air Arm. The Buccaneer S.2, first flown on 17 May 1963, has Spey turbofan engines, which give more power, lower fuel consumption, greater accelerating and climbing performance, and a marked increase in range. Eighty-four S. Mk 2's were built for the Royal Navy, equipping Nos 800, 801, 803 and 809 Squadrons. They entered service in October 1965. The Buccaneer's ground-hugging, under-the-radar penetration role at high subsonic speeds is well known, and its ordnance load may include nuclear weapons or four 1,000 lb bombs on its rotatable internal bay, with additional loads on four underwing pylons. The latter may comprise twelve 1,000 lb bombs, Bullpup missiles or pods of unguided rockets. A camera pack replaces the weapons in the internal bay when the Buccaneer is used for reconnaissance missions. Sixteen Buccaneer S.50's for Maritime Command of the South African Air Force were delivered during 1965. These are basically similar to the

S.2, and are fully 'navalised' although they operate from shore bases; they have a Bristol Siddeley BS.605 twin-barrelled rocket motor in the rear fuselage, which gives a thirty-second boost of 8,000 lb (3,628 kg) st to aid take-off.

In 1969 the hand-over began of Royal Navy Mk 2's to the RAF, the first RAF unit to be equipped being No 12 Squadron at Honington, which became operational with Buccaneers in July 1970. These aircraft are designated S. Mk 2A, and have various systems and equipment changes to meet RAF requirements. About sixty ex-RN Mk 2's are being converted to this initial standard and will eventually be brought up to S. Mk 2B standard, with the capability of carrying Martel anti-radar missiles, a bulged weapons bay door accommodating an additional fuel tank, and other airframe changes. In addition to these conversions, twenty-six new-production S. Mk 2B's were ordered for the RAF, the first of which made its first flight on 8 January 1970. A further sixteen were ordered in 1971. First RAF unit completely to re-equip with the S.2B was No 15 Squadron, formed in October 1970.

50 **Grumman A-6 Intruder**

Chosen late in 1957 from ten other designs, the Grumman A-6 has been well named. The first of eight A-6A (originally A2F-1) development aircraft (147864) flew on 19 April 1960; this aircraft featured downward-tilting rear ends to the engine tailpipes which would have given some 30 deg thrust deflection to aid take-off, but subsequent aircraft have had fixed pipes with a 7 deg deflection. Replacing the veteran Skyraider on US Navy attack carriers, the 2-seat Intruder entered service with VA-42 in February 1963, and by mid-1965 was flying combat missions in the Vietnam conflict, its qualities being well suited to operations in this kind of territory. The Intruder looks deceptively slight for the loads it can carry, but actually is slightly larger than the British Buccaneer, produced for a similar role with the Royal Navy and RAF. For carrier stowage, the Intruder's upward-folding wings reduce the span to 25 ft 2 in (7·67 m), and inboard of the fold lines are four stores stations; on these the aircraft may carry as many as thirty 500 lb bombs, pods each containing four 5 in Zuni rockets, Bullpup air-to-surface missiles or auxiliary fuel tanks; nuclear weapons may also be carried. There is a semi-recessed weapons bay in the fuselage. The standard US Navy version, the A-6A, is fitted with DIANE (Digital Integrated Attack Navigation Equipment). Subsequent versions have included the EA-6A, A-6B, EA-6B, A-6C, KA-6D and A-6E. The Marine Corps' EA-6A (twelve built) acts as an attack escort, using electronic countermeasures to protect the strike aircraft, and itself having a limited ability to deliver strike attacks. The A-6B is an A-6A variant with improved avionics, permitting the carriage of anti-radar missiles; the first example was flown in 1963. The prototype EA-6B

Prowler (149481) first flew on 25 May 1968, this version being an updated EA-6A with a 3 ft 4 in (1·02 m) longer nose and a 4-man crew. About thirty had been ordered up to 1971, and additional orders were expected to follow in FY 1972. Both EA models can be distinguished by the large radome mounted on top of the fin. The A-6C, another A-6A development, has an under-fuselage turret containing FLIR (forward-looking infra-red) sensors to detect 'difficult' targets, especially at night. The KA-6D, also an A-6A development, is in use as a carrier-borne flight refuelling tanker; and the A-6E (twenty-four ordered), which entered service in 1971, represents yet a further updating of avionics compared with the A-6A, and has improved weapon delivery. The total number of Intruders built prior to the A-6E order was four hundred and eighty-eight.

51 McDonnell Douglas A-4 Skyhawk

The little delta-winged Skyhawk was well nicknamed 'the bantam bomber' when it first appeared in the summer of 1954, and in 1972 it was well on the way to establishing an almost certain quarter-century of continuous production and/or service. Up to late 1971, more than two thousand five hundred Skyhawks had been built and delivered, and outstanding orders at that time were scheduled to keep the aircraft in production at least until 1974. The Skyhawk came into being, as the XA4D-1, basically

as a jet successor to the piston-engined Skyraider, another Douglas design, and the prototype was flown for the first time on 22 June 1954. Early models, before the new A-4 series designations were introduced in 1962, were the A4D-1 (one hundred and sixty-six built, including prototypes), A4D-2 (five hundred and forty-two built) and A4D-2N (six hundred and thirty-eight built); these became redesignated A-4A, A-4B and A-4C respectively. All were powered by variants of the Wright J65 engine, had a fixed armament of two 20 mm cannon in the wing roots, and three attachments for external stores – one under the fuselage and one beneath each wing. The first A-4A's entered service in October 1956 with US Navy Squadron VA-72; the A-4C, with a slightly lengthened nose, was the first model to have limited all-weather capability.

The designation A-4D was avoided, to prevent confusion with the original A4D styling, and the next major production model was the A-4E (originally A4D-5). This introduced a number of important changes, chief among which were the use of a Pratt & Whitney J52 as powerplant and two additional underwing stores pylons, thus increasing both range and effective payload. Four hundred and ninety-nine A-4E's were built, the first example being flown on 12 July 1961. Early in 1965 the US Navy ordered two TA-4E's, a 2-seat operational training version with lengthened fuselage and tandem seating. The production version of this was designated TA-4F: initial orders for one hundred and thirty-nine began to be delivered in May 1966, and subsequent contracts ensured that this version was still in production in 1971. The A-4F, first flown on 31 August 1966, was an updated single-seat attack model with many operational and avionics improvements including a 'saddle-back' humped fairing for avionics aft of the cockpit and armour protection and a zero-zero ejection seat for the pilot. One hundred and forty-six A-4F's were completed. A simplified trainer version, the TA-4J, was first flown in May 1969 and was still in production late in 1971. At that time the latest Sky-hawk model to be announced was the A-4M, also in current production, of which about fifty were being built for the US Marine Corps. The A-4M has a more powerful J52 engine of 11,200 lb (5,080 kg) st, deepened cockpit canopy, square-topped fin, brake parachute, increased ammunition for the 20 mm cannon and a number of other refinements. The first of two A-4M prototypes was flown on 10 April 1970, and deliveries began in the following November.

The gaps in the foregoing alphabetical sequence of variants are filled by converted and/or exported versions of the Skyhawk. The Argentine Air Force and Navy have, respectively, received fifty and twenty ex-USN A-4B's. The Royal Australian Navy has received sixteen A-4G's and four TA-4G's, of which half were newly-built and half ex-USN A-4F's and TA-4F's.

The A-4H is the version built for Israel (seventy, plus three TA-4H) it is based on the A-4E, but has a brake parachute, square-topped fin and 30 mm DEFA cannon. The Israeli Defence Force has also acquired about two dozen A-4E's which it is believed to be converting to A-4F configuration. The latest exports have been ten A-4K's and four TA-4K's to the Royal New Zealand Air Force, these corresponding broadly to the American F model and delivered in 1970.

52 **North American Rockwell A-5 Vigilante**

Making its maiden flight in XA3J-1 prototype form on 31 August 1958, the Vigilante is probably the most advanced carrier-based reconnaissance/strike aircraft in service today in any part of the world. Not long after its entry into US Navy service, with Heavy Attack Squadron VAH-7, in June 1961, the emphasis on the Vigilante's primary role was switched from attack, for which it was originally designed, to that of a Mach 2 reconnaissance aeroplane with a secondary strike capacity. To this end the fifty-five A-5A's and six A-5B's which constituted the first production models were converted to RA-5C's, and a further hundred or so aircraft were built as RA-5C's. A unique weapon delivery system was introduced at the outset of the Vigilante's design. This consisted of a linear tunnel running longitudinally from the central weapons bay between the two engine tail pipes, and through which the Vigilante's nuclear or high explosive stores could be ejected rearwards. The A-5B incorporated enlarged wing flaps and additional fuel tankage in a hump behind the second cockpit. These features, together with aerial reconnaissance cameras and side-looking airborne radar in a long ventral pack, also distinguish the RA-5C. The first RA-5C was flown on 30 June 1962, and this model entered service in June 1964 with RVAH-5 aboard the USS *Ranger*. Six or more RA-5C's were assigned to each 'Forrestal' class carrier, and in 1965 two of the smaller 'Midway' class began modernisation to enable them to operate Vigilantes. The Vigilante is operable over a wide speed range in all weathers, at high or low level, and carries a crew of 2. Range may be extended by underwing pylon tanks; in the attack role the four pylons may be used for napalm canisters, 1,000 lb or 2,000 lb bombs, or Bullpup air-to-surface missiles. In 1971 North American Rockwell put forward to the USAF a proposal for a Mach 2+ interceptor version of the Vigilante, designated NR-349 and having a third J79-GE-10 engine installed in the weapons bay.

53 Dassault Mirage III-R

As detailed in the companion volume *Fighters, Attack and Training Aircraft in Service since 1960*, the Dassault Mirage III/Mirage 5 family of combat aircraft has amassed orders for some twelve hundred aircraft since the first flight of the Mirage III prototype on 17 November 1956. Most of these fall into one or other of the categories covered by the volume mentioned, but a specialised tactical reconnaissance version has also been produced. This is the Mirage III-R, the prototype of which was flown on 31 October 1961 and the first production example on 1 February 1963. Externally recognisable by its snub nose, in which are installed three oblique and two vertical cameras, the reconnaissance version is based on the III-E airframe and has been built for the Armée de l'Air (fifty III-R and twenty III-RD) and for the air forces of Pakistan (three III-RP), South Africa (four III-RZ) and Switzerland (eighteen III-RS).

A reconnaissance version also exists of the simplified Mirage 5, and this has been ordered by Belgium (twenty-seven 5-BR), Colombia (5-COR) and Libya (5-DR).

54 Dassault Mirage IV-A

Spearhead of President de Gaulle's much-publicised *force de frappe*, the Mirage IV-A has given France, since the end of 1964, the means to deliver her own nuclear weapons. This medium range, Mach 2 strategic bomber is yet another variation on the remarkable Mirage theme, a new and advanced design in its own right but based on a scaled-up, twin-engined version of the delta-winged French fighter. Dassault began to design the bomber in 1957, and the prototype aircraft made its maiden flight some 2 years later, on 17 June 1959, powered by two 13,228 lb (6,000 kg)

Atar 09 engines. The three evaluation aircraft which followed were very slightly larger, had more powerful Atar 09C or 09K engines and embodied various design improvements, and the first of fifty production Mirage IV-A's was flown on 7 December 1963. Towards the end of 1964 these aircraft began to enter service with the 92nd Escadre of the Commandement des Forces Aériennes Stratégiques, deliveries continuing to the 91st Escadre during 1965. A follow-on order for twelve more aircraft was also started in 1965, and all sixty-two had been delivered by 1967. The Mirage IV-A has a 2-man crew, and an unrefuelled range of about 1,000 miles; it can, however, operate over much greater ranges by working in collaboration with C-135F tanker aircraft. The weapon which it was designed to carry is a fifty-kiloton free-fall device and is mounted semi-recessed under the fuselage; alternative loads can include four Anglo-French Martel air-to-surface missiles, or sixteen 450 kg conventional high-explosive bombs under the fuselage and wings. Forward of the under-fuselage weapon attachment point is a flat circular CSF radar fairing. The Mirage IV-A can take off normally from runways of 2,625 ft (800 m) length, or can operate out of smaller airfields by the use of up to twelve JATO bottles mounted under the rear fuselage.

55 Tupolev Tu-16 ('Badger')

With nearly two decades of service life behind it, the Tu-16 has been only partially replaced by the Tu-22 Blinder as the standard medium-range reconnaissance bomber of the Soviet air arms, and several hundreds were estimated to be still active at the end of 1971. Produced originally for the V-VS's Dalnaya Aviatsiya, or Long Range Aviation, the Tu-16 began in the early 1960s a new lease of operational life as an anti-shipping bomber with the A-VMF, or Soviet Naval Aviation. About two thousand Tu-16's are believed to have been built. The Tu-16 first entered service with the Soviet Air Force in 1954-55, the first production version being known as Badger-A. Carrying a 6- or 7-man crew, the Badger-A has a built-in defensive armament of twin 23 mm cannon in dorsal, ventral and tail positions, with a seventh gun on the starboard side of the nose; a 21 ft (6·40 m) weapons bay accommodates a maximum 19,840 lb (9,000 kg) war load. About twenty Badger-A's, supplied to the Egyptian Air Force, were destroyed in the 'six-day war' of 1967, but were subsequently replaced; six others were supplied to Iraq. A number of Soviet Air Force machines have been converted for the reconnaissance role with additional radar and long-range fuel tanks, and all versions of the Tu-16 so far identified have in-flight refuelling capability. Badger-B is a naval conversion carrying two 'Kennel' anti-shipping missiles on pylons outboard of the main undercarriage fairings, and is the model which also equipped two squadrons of the Angkatan Udara Republik Indonesia from 1961. A more extensive conversion is the Badger-C, which features a large search radar in a longer, solid nose, and is a carrier for the 'Kipper' stand-off anti-shipping missile, one weapon being attached beneath the centre fuselage. Pairs of Badgers have frequently been observed on long-range naval patrol, fitted with auxiliary fuel tanks and fairings which contain electronic counter-measures equipment. ECM recon-naissance models so far identified include Badger-D and -E, similar to Badger-C but with various under-fuselage fairings, and Badger-F, which carries ECM pods on wing-mounted pylons but otherwise appears similar to Badger-A.

56 Tupolev Tu-22 ('Blinder')

Believed to have flown in prototype form in the late 1950s, and to have entered Soviet Air Force service in about 1964–65, the Blinder is a medium-range tactical strike and reconnaissance aircraft which has been compared, from a functional viewpoint, with America's B-58 Hustler. Aesthetically and aero-dynamically the Blinder is more attractive than the Hustler, though its performance is lower and its range of weapons is more restricted. Knowledge of the Blinder was based initially on the appearance of ten of these aircraft at Tushino in 1961. One of these, since identified by NATO as Blinder-B, was carry-ing a single 'Kitchen' stand-off bomb semi-recessed beneath its belly. The other nine, which had numerous under-fuselage ports for cameras or visual bomb-aiming and

a smaller radar in the nose, were later dubbed Blinder-A. At Domo-dedovo in 1967 the flying display included twenty-two Tu-22's; these were mostly of the Blinder-B model, and revealed also a nose-mounted flight refuelling probe. Defensive armament of the Blinder is limited to a single 23 mm radar-directed gun in the extreme tail. A third version, Blinder-C, has since been identified. This is an operational training version, distinguished by its 'stepped' crew enclosure em-bodying a raised rear cockpit for the second pilot. The combat ver-sions are thought to carry a crew of 3. Although it does not appear to have replaced the Tu-16 (which continues in wide-scale service) to anything like the extent first anti-cipated by many western judges, the Tu-22 nevertheless is in service both with medium bomber/recon-naissance formations of the Soviet Air Force and, as a maritime strike/reconnaissance aircraft (and pos-sibly for ECM reconnaissance as well), with shore-based units of the A-VMF.

57 Douglas A-3 Skywarrior and B-66 Destroyer

The Skywarrior has a long history, having resulted from a 1947 US Navy requirement for a new carrier-based attack aircraft to combine jet power with the ability to deliver nuclear weapons. After some 2 years of preliminary design work Douglas was awarded a contract in March 1949 to develop and build two prototypes. The first of these (125412), the XA3D-1, was flown for the first time on 28 October 1952, powered by two 7,000 lb (3,175 kg) st Westinghouse XJ40-WE-3 turbojets in underwing pods. Because of the ultimate abandonment of the J40 engine programme, a switch was made to the 9,700 lb (4,400 kg) st Pratt & Whitney J57-P-6, the YA3D-1 production prototype flying with this powerplant on 16 September 1953. Two hundred and eighty production Skywarriors were built subsequently; these (with their pre-1962 designations in parentheses) comprised fifty A-3A (A3D-1), one hundred and sixty-four A-3B (A3D-2), thirty RA-3B (A3D-2P), twenty-four EA-3B (A3D-2Q) and twelve TA-3B (A3D-2T). The A-3A's were delivered from March 1956, the first US Navy unit to receive them being VAH-1. Conversions included five to EA-3A (A3D-1Q), with electronic countermeasures (ECM) gear in the tailcone in place of the A-3A's twin 20 mm remote-controlled guns; one to YRA-3A (A3D-1P) as a photo-reconnaissance prototype; and others to TA-3A (A3D-1T) dual-control trainers. The definitive Navy version was the A-3B, with more powerful J57-P-10 engines, a modified weapons bay to carry a greater variety of stores, and provision for in-flight refuelling; like the A-3A, it carried a crew of 3. Deliveries of the A-3B, to Squadron VAH-2, began in January 1957, and eventually eight heavy attack squadrons, on board the 'Essex' and 'Midway' class carriers, were equipped with the A-3B. Whereas,

in the A-3A and A-3B, only the crew compartment was pressurised, the whole fuselage became so in the three subsequent production models. This was brought about by their specialised roles, which called for 'mission kits' and appropriate additional crew members to be installed in the weapons bay. The photo-reconnaissance RA-3B, first flown on 22 July 1958, thus carried 2 operators and twelve vertical or oblique cameras in this position; the EA-3B, first flown on 10 December 1958, carried ECM equipment and 4 operators, making a crew total of 7; the TA-3B, first flown on 29 August 1959, was essentially an operational trainer for the EA-3B and carried a pilot, 1 instructor and 6 trainees. One TA-3B was converted to VA-3B, equipped as an executive transport. By 1971 those Skywarriors still in service were employed primarily in the electronics reconnaissance role in Vietnam or as KA-3 or EKA-3 flight refuelling tankers.

In February 1952 the US Air Force decided to adopt the Skywarrior to meet its own requirement for the tactical light bomber and reconnaissance roles. Although considerable internal redesign was involved, additional prototypes were not considered necessary. Instead, the USAF ordered five RB-66A Destroyers for service evaluation. The first of these (52–2828) was flown on 28 June 1954, the most noticeable external difference between the Destroyer and its naval counterpart being the increased-length pods of the engines, which in the RB-66A were Allison YJ71-A-9's of 9,700 lb (4,400 kg) st. Contracts for four production versions of the Destroyer eventually totalled two hundred and eighty-nine, comprising one hundred and forty-five RB-66B, seventy-two B-66B, and thirty-six each of the RB-66C and WB-66D. In the event, however, some of these contracts were cut back, and Destroyer production ended in June 1958 after the completion of two hundred and nine aircraft, including the original five RB-66A's. The first RB-66B was flown on 4 January 1955, deliveries beginning in February 1956 and eventually equipping three squadrons of the 10th Tactical Reconnaissance Wing in Europe. A few of the early RB-66B's continued to use the Allison J71-A-9, but most were fitted with the more powerful J71-A-13 of 10,200 lb (4,626 kg) st. This day/night photographic reconnaissance model was followed in March 1956 by first deliveries of the B-66B tactical light bomber, and two months later by the electronics-reconnaissance RB-66C, which had first flown on 29 October 1955. The RB-66C, carrying a four-men-plus-equipment package in the weapons bay, could be distinguished by radar fairings at each wingtip and beneath the fuselage. The WB-66D, first flown on 27 May 1957, with deliveries beginning in the following month, was a weather reconnaissance version carrying an equipment package and two operators in the weapons bay. Two WB-66D's were converted in 1962-63 as Northrop X-21A laminar flow wing

research aircaft. In 1971 the primary role of those Destroyers still in service was, like that of their naval counterparts, the task of electronics reconnaissance in South-east Asia, under designations which included EB-66B, C and F.

58 **Yakovlev Yak-28 ('Brewer')**
At Kubinka in June 1956, after the Aviation Day display, the Soviet authorities exhibited an attack version of the Yak-25 fighter (the Yak-25R or Flashlight-B) and another twin-jet, swept-wing aeroplane reputedly of Ilyushin design which the western powers codenamed 'Blowlamp'. In the event, only the former of these was accepted for service, but at Tushino in 1961 the Russians revealed further developments of the Yak-25 which at first were all believed to be fighters and were given the name Firebar. Three of these machines were alike in having transparent nose stations; two of them (originally Firebar-A and -C) were later recognised to have been light bombers and were given the new code name 'Brewer'. This aircraft is now identified as the Yak-28; the Firebar all-weather fighter, or Yak-28P, is a variant of this basic design and is described in the companion to this volume. The Brewer, via the Yak-26 'Mangrove', thus represents a third-generation development of the original Yak-25 design, in which the wing is modified in planform, has greater area, is mounted higher on the fuselage, and supports larger and more powerful afterburning engines. The fin area is greater, the

fuselage noticeably longer, and the main landing gear is different. The Yak-28 is a 2-seater, has an internal weapons bay (which can probably accommodate a load of about 2,200 lb = 1,000 kg) and two underwing store-points for bombs, rockets or guided missiles. Defensive armament comprises one or two 30 mm cannon, mounted in the fuselage below and just ahead of the wing roots. The Brewer entered service with Frontovaya Aviatsiya units of the V-VS as an Il-28 replacement in about 1962–63; there have been no reports of it being supplied as a similar replacement to Communist-sympathetic air forces.

59 Yakovlev 'Mandrake'

It was known in Western circles since the early 1960s that the Soviet Air Force had in service a high altitude strategic reconnaissance aeroplane designed to carry out broadly similar functions to those of the American Lockheed U-2. No photographs of it have been released for publication, and estimates of its size, configuration and performance have been made on the basis of such meagre details of its appearance as have been reported verbally. From these it is known that Mandrake is basically a derivative of the Yak-25 'Flashlight' all-weather fighter, utilising the same fuselage and tail assembly as the Yak-25R Flashlight-B or Yak-26 Mangrove, with a 'solid' nose to house its reconnaissance gear, and married to an unswept, long-span wing to confer the necessary high-altitude capability. There is reason

to believe that the so-called 'RV' aircraft which set two height-with-payload records in the summer of 1959 was a variant of the Mandrake, and this assumption, based on the use of similar engines to those in the Flashlight-B, indicates that the Mandrake is probably intended to cruise at about 475 mph (765 km/hr) at around 60,000 ft (18,000 m). The most reasonable explanation for converting an obsolete warplane to achieve such a modest performance seems to be that the single-seat Mandrake was intended primarily for Chinese or East European border missions where it was not likely to encounter sophisticated interception systems. This explanation appears to be borne out by the location of actual sightings.

60 General Dynamics (Martin) RB-57

The innovations and elongations introduced by Martin and Convair engineers on the willing Canberra airframe during the past 20 years make it difficult to recognise, in some of the final models, any connection at all with William Petter's original design. After building seventy-five B/RB-57A's virtually to the Canberra B.2 pattern (except for a change of powerplant), Martin introduced the first US modifications on its main production version, the B-57B, of which two hundred and two were built. This intruder bomber had a new, 2-man, tandem-seat cockpit, pylons for underwing stores, eight 0·5 in guns in the wing leading edges and a Martin-designed rotating bomb door on

140

which the aeroplane's 6,000 lb (2,722 kg) internal load was carried. B-57B's were supplied to the Chinese Nationalist, Pakistan and Vietnamese Air Forces, and a number were recalled from the Air National Guard for active bomber duties in the mid-1960s. Thirty-eight B-57C's were basically the same aeroplane fitted with dual controls. Martin then built twenty RB-57D's, in both single- and 2-seat forms, which had 11,000 lb (4,990 kg) st J57-P-37A engines and a 106 ft (32·31 m) wing span as compared with the original's 64 ft (19·51 m). This model was intended for photographic and electronics reconnaissance duties, and two were supplied to the Chinese Nationalist Air Force; the rest served with Air Defense Command and the Pacific Air Force. The B-57E designation covered sixty-eight examples of a target-towing adaptation of the B-57B. In June 1964 General Dynamics (Convair) delivered to the 58th Weather Reconnaissance Squadron the first of a dozen RB-57F's, a further B-57B conversion with an enormous 122 ft 5 in (37·32 m) span wing, revised vertical tail surfaces, turbofan main engines and two auxiliary turbojets in underwing pods. These aircraft were for strategic as well as weather reconnaissance, and for air sampling at extreme altitudes. Further-modified versions of the B-57B, used in South-east Asia, have included the EB-57B for electronic countermeasures and the Westinghouse/ Martin B-57G, which has a much-modified nose section with radar and sensor fairings, laser range-finder, and infra-red and other detection gear for night interdiction.

61 Kawasaki C-1A

Ever since it was re-formed after World War 2, the Japan Air Self Defence Force has relied for its main transport commitment, apart from a few YS-11A's, on the ageing Curtiss C-46 whose origins go back to 1939. That situation will be remedied with the entry into service in 1974 of the twin-turbofan C-1A, about forty of which are due to be procured in annual batches. The basic design work, begun in 1966, was undertaken by the Nihon Aircraft Manufacturing Company (NAMC), and Mitsubishi completed a full-scale mock-up of the aircraft in March 1968. In the following autumn NAMC began construction of two XC-1 prototypes, which made their first flights on 12 November 1970 and 16 January 1971, and a third airframe for static testing. Service evaluation by the Japan Defence Agency started in the spring of 1971, and the first of the production C-1A's is due to fly in 1973. These are the responsibility of Kawasaki, although the production task is being shared with Fuji (outer wings), Mitsubishi (centre and aft fuselage and tail), Nippi (flaps, ailerons, engine pylons and pods), Shin Meiwa (palletised cargo-loading system) and Sumitomo (landing gear). Kawasaki is building the forward fuselage and wing centre-section, and is responsible for final assembly and pre-delivery flight testing. The C-1A carries a crew of 5, including a cargo supervisor, and is able to carry up to 60 troops, 45 para-troops, 36 casualty litters and their attendants, Army vehicles and equipment, or palletised cargo up to a normal maximum payload of 17,640 lb (8,000 kg). The JASDF's stated requirements include, in addition to the C-1A transport, other aircraft for ECM duties and weather reconnaissance. The C-1A may also be ordered as an AEW and mine-laying aircraft by the Maritime Self Defence Force.

62 Lockheed S-3 Viking

Five of America's major aircraft manufacturers submitted proposals in April 1968 to meet the US Navy's requirement for a replacement for the venerable Grumman S-2 Tracker in the carrier-borne ASW role. In the following autumn the choice was reduced to the compet-ing designs of General Dynamics (Convair) and Lockheed, and the latter company was finally selected by Naval Air Systems Command to develop the new aircraft. The initial contract called for the completion of six development aircraft (later increased to eight), and up to the spring of 1972 US Navy orders and options for the S-3A totalled one hundred and ninety-one production examples. A full-sized mock-up of the S-3A was completed in 1970, and the colour illustration is based upon details released up to that time. The first of the development aircraft (157992) was rolled out in November 1971 and flew for the first time on 21 January 1972; de-

liveries to the USN are scheduled to begin in late 1973. The initial S-3A version of the Viking carries a crew of 4, each on a zero-zero ejection seat; its ASW equip-ment includes an on-board com-puter and data processer, and the latest and most sensitive MAD gear, acoustic and non-acoustic sensors, ECM gear and radar. A divided weapons bay in the centre fuselage can accommodate four bombs, mines, depth charges or torpedoes, and there is a pylon beneath each wing for carrying mines, cluster bombs, rocket pods, flare launchers or auxiliary fuel tanks. There is a considerable stretch potential in the Viking's design which will allow for an increase of the gross weight up to 50,000 lb (22,680 kg) and of the initial electronics by some 50 per cent. Later versions are foreseen to fulfil such roles as flight refuelling tanker, utility transport, ASW com-mand and control or ECM patrol and monitoring.

63 Dassault Mystère 20/ Falcon 20

Work on building a prototype of this rear-engined light executive aero-plane began in January 1962, and the completed aircraft flew for the first time on 4 May 1963, powered by 3,300 lb (1,489 kg) st Pratt & Whitney JT12A-8 engines. On 10 July 1964 it was reflown with General Electric CF700 turbofans and various structural changes, including an 18 in (0·45 m) cabin extension, a 3 ft 3¼ in (1·00 m) in-crease in wing span, and a strength-ened undercarriage. By February

1972 the order book stood at two hundred and eighty-two aircraft, most of them bought by the Business Jets Division of Pan American Airways for re-sale in the civil market. Military and government orders up to the end of 1971 included seven for the Armée de l'Air, three as aircrew trainers for No 34 Squadron of the RAAF, seven for No 412 Squadron of the Canadian Armed Forces (who have options on a further fourteen), two for the Moroccan Ministry of National Defence, three for the Central African Republic, one for the Algerian government and one for the air force of the Ivory Coast. The Falcon, in which Mme Jacqueline Auriol set two international closed-circuit speed records in June 1965, carries a crew of 2 and, in its passenger configuration, seats up to 10 people. Two of the Armée de l'Air machines are Falcon ST's, a modified version with pointed nose radomes and equipped as flying classrooms for operational and navigation training of Mirage III combat pilots. Two similar aircraft have been ordered by Libya.

64 BAC VC10

Brize Norton, Oxfordshire, home of No 10 Squadron, RAF Air Support Command, is the headquarters of the fourteen VC10's delivered to the Royal Air Force during 1966–68. This was the only military order to be placed for a jet transport whose passenger appeal in the civil market was almost as marked as that of its turboprop-engined ancestor, the Viscount, some dozen years pre-

viously. The first prototype of the VC10 made its maiden flight on 29 June 1962, that of the first aircraft for the RAF (XR806) taking place on 26 November 1965, with deliveries to Transport Command (as it then was) starting on 7 July 1966. Although basically a standard VC10, with rearward-facing seats for 150 passengers, the Model 1106 for the RAF also embodies a number of features of the Super VC10, including Conway RCo.43 by-pass engines with thrust reversal on the outer pair, a fin fuel tank, extended wing leading edges and in-flight refuelling capabilities. Intended primarily for personnel transport over long ranges, the Belfast being the RAF's standard heavy freight transport, the VC10 nevertheless has a large forward cargo door and reinforced flooring. Air Support Command aircraft, named individually after air holders of the Victoria Cross, are designated VC10 C. Mk 1. One aircraft was employed from 1969 as a flying testbed for the Rolls-Royce RB.211 turbofan engine. A description of the VC10 and Super VC10 commercial models appears in the companion volume *Airliners since 1946*.

65 Hawker Siddeley Vulcan

Two of the notable qualities of this remarkable aeroplane, which still draw respect from an observer, are its extremely modest runway requirements and its considerable manoeuvrability in the air. The transonic Vulcan is the world's largest operational delta-winged aeroplane, and entered Bomber

Command service in the middle 1950s. It was designed by the former Avro company, the Avro 698 first prototype (VX770) making its maiden flight on 30 August 1952 powered by four Rolls-Royce Avon engines. The second prototype (first flight 3 September 1953) and subsequent aircraft all had Bristol Siddeley Olympus turbojets. Production of the Vulcan B. Mk 1 began in 1953; forty-five were built, the first operational unit being No 83 Squadron in mid-1957. The B. Mk 1's were subsequently modified to B. Mk 1A standard, with electronic countermeasures equipment in a bulged tail cone. By the mid-1960s all Mk 1/1A Vulcans had been placed on the reserve. Their place in the front-line strategic V-bomber force was then occupied by the B. Mk 2 which has a 12 ft 0 in (3·66 m) greater wing spread and more powerful Olympus engines. Deliveries of the Vulcan B.2, which began in July 1960, were made to Nos 9, 12, 27, 35, 44, 50, 83, 101 and 617 Squadrons, the total number built being about a hundred. Whereas the Mks 1/1A were able to carry free-falling nuclear weapons or 21,000 lb (9,525 kg) of conventional high explosive bombs, the Vulcan B.2 was equipped also to carry the British powered stand-off bomb, Blue Steel. Both marks of Vulcan were, while in service, refitted with successively more powerful variants of the Olympus jet engine, and the Mk 2 with capacity for in-flight refuelling. In 1971 RAF Strike Command retained only two Blue Steel-equipped Vul-

can squadrons, its five remaining squadrons (three in the UK and two in Cyprus) by then fulfilling a tactical rather than a strategic bombing role.

66 Handley Page Victor

The Victor, third of Britain's trio of V-bombers, was first flown in prototype form (WB771) on 24 December 1952 and became operational with RAF Bomber Command (now Strike Command) in the spring of 1958, four squadrons (Nos 10, 15, 55 and 57) being operational by 1960. These were equipped with the Sapphire-engined B. Mks 1 and 1A, the latter model differing in internal equipment and in having ECM gear in the tail-cone. A number of these early Victors later served in the Far East, where they formed part of the V-bomber detachment operating with SEATO. Most of them, however, were eventually converted as reconnaissance aircraft, serving as B.(P.R.) Mks 1 and 1A with the Photographic Flight at Wyton; or as three-point refuelling tankers (designated K.1A). The major bomber version was the B. Mk 2, first flown on 20 February 1959, which became operational in February 1964. This has a 10 ft 0 in (3·05 m) greater wing span, larger air intakes, Conway turbofan engines, and (since conversion in 1963) blister fairings above the outer wing trailing edges. These blisters have a dual purpose, for as well as reducing drag they contain 'window' which can be dispersed in the wake of the bomber to confuse the radar of a pursuing interceptor. The Victor B. Mk 2 was designed to deliver the Blue Steel stand-off bomb, which it carried semi-externally, but it could instead carry, internally, various free-falling nuclear weapons or thirty-five 1,000 lb high explosive bombs, operating at either high or low level. Overall Victor production is believed to have been in the region of one hundred and twenty, probably in the approximate ratio of two Mks 1/1A to one Mk 2. The B. 2 was withdrawn from RAF bomber squadrons in 1969, but still serves in small numbers as a strategic reconnaissance aircraft (B.(S.R.) Mk 2) and three-point refuelling tanker (K. Mk 2).

67 Boeing B-52 Stratofortress

Boeing's giant B-52 seems almost certain to go down in history as the last of the big 'heavies', such have been the changes in global strategy since it first entered US Air Force service in the summer of 1955. Certainly the use of a 200 ton, eight-engined, inter-continental bomber to drop propaganda leaflets or even bombs over North Vietnam is the antithesis of cost-effectiveness, as events have demonstrated all too clearly – though nothing could be further from the role which the B-52 was designed to perform. The first XB-52 prototype was flown on 2 October 1952, and was followed by a single YB-52, three B-52A's and fifty examples of the initial production model, the B-52B. Strategic Air Command had in service in 1971 about five hundred B-52's,

approximately two-fifths of these being the tall-finned B-52C, D, E and F models (respective production totals were thirty-five, one hundred and seventy, one hundred, and eighty-eight); these differ from one another mainly in such matters as engine power, electronics and other equipment and have a maximum internal bomb load of 65,000 lb (29,484 kg). The remainder are B-52G's or B-52H's, of which the former has a marked performance increase and a cropped vertical tail, and was the first Stratofortress model to carry the Hound Dog stand-off missile. Two of these weapons are carried underwing, one between the fuselage and the inner pair of engine pods on each side. The B-52G's internal load can include two Quail decoy missiles and 20,000 lb (9,072 kg) of free-fall bombs, and a multi-barrel 20 mm cannon protects the bomber from the rear. Decoy rockets may also be carried beneath the wings. One hundred and ninety-three B-52G's were built, the first example being flown on 26 October 1958 and the first deliveries to SAC being made in the following February. The final version, which appeared in 1959, is the B-52H, one hundred and two of which were built up to June 1962. This model is essentially similar to the G except that it has turbofan engines, which increase the range and general performance still further. The B-52H, first flown on 6 March 1961, has flown unrefuelled for a distance of more than 12,500 miles (20,117 km). All B-52's still in service have been modernised and strengthened structurally to enable them to carry out low-level penetration missions. The Stratofortress is scheduled to remain in service, in gradually diminishing numbers as the earlier variants are phased out, until the mid-1970s. Ninety-six G and H models are the subject of a modernisation programme to enable them to carry up to twenty SRAMs (Short-Range Attack Missiles), six under each wing and eight internally. Another modification programme will provide 'chin' turrets containing infra-red detection equipment.

68 Boeing Stratotanker (KC-135) and Stratolifter (C-135)

This military counterpart of the Boeing 707 airliner, which has the Boeing Model number 717, is in use by the US Air Force in a considerable variety of roles, its total production having amounted to eight hundred and six. By far the most prolific version is the KC-135A flight refuelling tanker, which first flew on 31 August 1956; an overall total of seven hundred and thirty-two KC-135A's were built before production ended in December 1964. They have been in service since June 1957, and are currently able to refuel other aircraft by the probe-and-drogue method as well as by the familiar 'butterfly boom' beneath the rear fuselage. The KC-135A can be used as a long-range transport, but there are also specialised transport models. These include fifteen new and three converted C-135A's (first flight 19

May 1961) and thirty fan-engined C-135B's (first flight 12 February 1962), the latter's capacity being 126 troops, 44 casualty litters or 87,100 lb (39,508 kg) of freight. Twelve C-135F tankers, generally similar to the A model, were supplied to the Armée de l'Air to act as a tanker fleet for the Mirage IV-A bomber force. The last USAF production model of the Boeing 717 (seventeen built) was the EC-135C (originally KC-135B) airborne command post. Boeing Model number 739 identifies four RC-135A and ten RC-135B built, respectively, for the Air Photographic and Charting Service of MAC and for electronic reconnaissance.

Aircraft converted for special functions have resulted in many new designations, including EC-135A (six, airborne command post/communications relay), JKC-135A and NKC-135A (special test), VC-135B (eleven, VIP transport), WC-135B (ten, weather reconnaissance), RC-135C (ten, electronic reconnaissance), RC-135D (four, ditto), RC-135E (one, ditto), EC-135G (four, airborne command post/communications relay), EC-135H (five, airborne command post), EC-135J (three, ditto), EC-135K (one, ditto), EC-135L (three, airborne command post/communications relay), RC-135M (special mission), EC-135N (eight, radio/telemetry for Apollo space programme), EC-135P (five, airborne command post), KC-135Q (tanker for SR-71), KC-135R (special reconnaissance), RC-135S (ditto) and KC-135T (ELINT collection).

In addition to the above, several examples of the commercial Boeing 707 have been supplied to meet military orders. Up to mid-1971 such orders had included three short-fuselage 707-153's as VC-137A (VC-137B after conversion to turbofans) and one Presidential 707-353 (VC-137C) for the USAF; and other 707-320 series to the Federal German Luftwaffe (four), Canadian Armed Forces (five), and Portuguese Air Force (two). Two other Boeing 707-320 airframes have undergone conversion to become EC-137D aerodynamic prototypes of Boeing's new AWACS (Airborne Warning and Control System) patrol aircraft for the USAF.

69 Hawker Siddeley Comet and Nimrod

With the Belfast and VC10, the Comets in Transport Command service gave the RAF a highly effective long-range strategic transport force, capable of transferring men and equipment to any part of the world in a short space of time. The Comet force included, at its peak, eleven C. Mk 2, three of which were assigned to No 90 (Signals) Group but available for transport duty if required; two T. Mk 2 crew trainers; and five C. Mk 4. The C.2's, ex-airline machines which entered RAF service with No 216 Squadron in 1956, had capacity for 48 passengers, or 36 passengers and 11,200 lb (5,080 kg) of cargo; they were retired in 1967. The C.4's, acquired in 1962 and still serving in 1971, have maximum seating for 94 people in addition to the crew of 5, and have strengthened floors for cargo carrying.

Early in 1965 the British government authorised development of the basic Comet design, as the Hawker Siddeley 801, to provide a maritime reconnaissance replacement for the ageing early marks of the Shackleton. As a first stage, two Comet 4C airliners were converted in 1965–66 to have a modified fuselage with internal provision for search and reconnaissance equipment and accommodation for the crews during long patrols. The first of these prototypes (XV147) was flown on 23 May 1967, and was powered by Rolls-Royce Spey turbofan engines, as specified for production aircraft. The second prototype, which followed it on 31 July 1967, was used primarily to test the maritime equipment and retained its original Avon engines. The major production version is the Nimrod MR. Mk 1; the first example (XV226) flew on 28 June 1968, and deliveries to RAF Strike Command began in October 1969, the first operational unit being No 201 Squadron. Thirty-eight MR. Mk 1's were ordered initially; they were followed by three specially-equipped R. Mk 1's, delivered in 1971 to No 51 Squadron and officially described as radio/radar calibration aircraft, although they may also be fulfilling an electronics reconnaissance role. In January 1972 it was announced that a further batch of eight Nimrod MR. Mk 1's were to be built for the RAF, which will then have six squadrons equipped with this version. From the Comet airframe, the

Nimrod retains largely unchanged the wing and horizontal tail surfaces and, in strengthened form, the landing gear. The fuselage contours are new, and are made up essentially of a pressurised upper shell inherited from the Comet and an unpressurised lower shell containing the weapons bay and much of the maritime equipment. A large dorsal fin has been added, the main fin is topped by a streamlined ECM pod, and an MAD tailboom (not on the R. Mk 1) is fitted. The Nimrod carries a crew of 12, and its 50 ft (15·25 m) weapons bay can accommodate a wide range of ASW weapons including bombs, mines, depth charges and homing torpedoes. Additionally, a pylon under each wing, just outboard of the main landing gear units, can be used to carry an AS.12 or other air-to-surface missile. Provision is made for the carriage of 45 troops in a secondary transport role.

70 **Myasishchev Mya-4 ('Bison')**

Considering the degree of attention and speculation that usually surrounds the appearance of any new Soviet military aircraft, comparatively little is known of the four-jet Mya-4 designed by V. M. Myasishchev, though its existence first became known to the west more than a decade and a half ago. Its first public appearance was in the flypast over Moscow on May Day 1954, in which a prototype, designated TsAGI 428, took part, and production examples began to enter

service with units of the Dalnaya Aviatsiya (Long Range Aviation) in 1955–56. Of comparable purpose to the USAF's B-52 Stratofortress, the Mya-4 carried a crew of at least 8, and at least one feature which it shared with the B-52 was a similar undercarriage configuration, with 'bicycle'-type tandem main-wheel bogies in the fuselage, fore and aft of the weapons bay, and outboard supporting wheels housed in the pod fairings at the wingtips. Power plant was four 19,180 lb (8,700 kg) st Mikulin AM-3D turbo-jet engines. The Bison could carry a maximum bomb load in the region of 9,920 lb (4,500 kg), and because of its comparatively low operational ceiling was equipped for defence with radar-directed barbettes above and below the fuseage, fore and aft of the wings, each with twin 23 mm guns, and a further pair of similar guns in a manually-directed tail turret. Some aircraft were fitted with a single, fixed gun in the starboard side of the nose. The Mya-4 was equipped for in-flight refuelling, and possessed an intercontinental range with a conventional or nuclear bomb load, but it is not thought to have been built in large numbers for the strategic bomber role, in which it is code-named Bison-A. During the late 'fifties and early 'sixties, however, it began to be used as a flight refuelling tanker and, increasingly, by units of the A-VMF (Soviet Naval Aviation) as a maritime reconnaissance bomber (Bison-B). In the latter capacity it was still in use at the end of the 1960s, when the number in service was estimated at slightly more than a hundred.

As early as 1959 a series of international speed-with-payload and height-with-payload records were set up by Myasishchev aircraft designated 103-M and 201-M, powered by D-15 turbojet engines. Not until 8 years later did one of these aircraft appear in public, when a single 201-M was exhibited at the Aviation Day display at Domodedovo in July 1967. It was then immediately apparent that this was a variant of the Mya-4, from which it differed principally in having an extended and redesigned nose section incorporating a fixed flight-refuelling probe and a large search radar. This aircraft forms the subject of the colour illustration. The 201-M is not believed to be a production version as such, but some of the Mya-4's remaining in A-VMF service have been fitted with similar nose sections and are designated Bison-C.

71 Lockheed C-141 StarLifter

The first jet aircraft designed from the outset as a military cargo aeroplane, the StarLifter's purpose is to provide fast transportation over global ranges for the USAF Military Airlift Command and on strategic routes for Strike Command. It is not the largest-capacity US transport, this distinction now belonging to the later C-5A Galaxy, but it is much faster than earlier transport aircraft. This was graphically demonstrated by a C-141 which transported a 50,000 lb (22,680 kg) payload over 7,500 miles (12,070 km),

a feat which it accomplished in 18¼ flying hours; a similar operation would have taken 30½ hours by Hercules or 41¾ hours by Globemaster. An 88,000 lb (39,916 kg) Minuteman container, 154 troops, 127 paratroops, 80 casualty litters with medical staff, or a 94,000 lb (42,638 kg) cargo load, are all within the StarLifter's capacity; and the aircraft can be unloaded, re-loaded and ready for take-off in less than half an hour. A flight crew of 4 is carried, together with a relief crew for very long range missions. The C-141 was declared the winner of a USAF design competition in March 1961, and the first of five development aircraft was flown on 17 December 1963. Production C-141A's became operational with the 44th and 75th Air Transport Squadrons of Military Airlift Command in 1965, and in August of that year were operating in Vietnam. One hundred and thirty-two C-141A's were ordered initially by the US Air Force, a reduction on the original requirement due to procurement of the giant C-5A to follow in the late 1960s; but this was later increased to a total of two hundred and eighty-four, which were to equip fourteen MAC squadrons. Production was completed in late 1967.

72 Lockheed C-5 Galaxy

Currently the world's largest military transport aircraft, and exceeded in size and gross weight only by later models of the commercial Boeing 747, the Galaxy came into being as the result of the CX-4 requirement issued by the USAF's Military Air Transport Service (now Military Airlift Command) in 1963 for a large logistics transport aircraft. This and other requirements were subsequently combined in a revised requirement, CX-HLS (Cargo Experimental-Heavy Logistics System), for which Boeing, Douglas and Lockheed were invited in 1964 to develop their initial designs further. At the same time, General Electric and Pratt & Whitney were invited to develop an appropriate powerplant for the aircraft. By the end of 1965 the choice had been made of a Lockheed/General Electric association to proceed to the hardware stage with what was then known officially as the C-5A Galaxy. Eight test and evaluation aircraft were built, construction beginning in August 1966 and being followed by the flight of the first Galaxy on 30 June 1968. All eight aircraft were assigned to the flight test programme, which extended into mid-1971. Some eighteen months before this, however, the first of eighty-one production C-5A's so far ordered had been delivered to the USAF, on 17 December 1969. The USAF is scheduled to have four operational Galaxy squadrons, and the first two of these, based at Charleston AFB, South Carolina, and Travis AFB, California, were already carrying out regular operations to and from South-east Asia and Europe by mid-1971. A second squadron was eventually to be based at Travis AFB, and the fourth at Dover AFB, Delaware.

An important factor in the CX-HLS specification was that the Galaxy should, despite its greater size, be capable of operating from the same 8,000 ft (2,440 m) runways as the C-141 StarLifter, and of landing on semi-prepared runways in combat areas of no more than 4,000 ft (1,220 m). To distribute runway load, the Galaxy has a 28-wheel landing gear, consisting of a 4-wheel nose unit and four 6-wheel main bogies. It carries a normal crew of 5, with a rest area at the front of the upper deck for up to 15 people, including a relief crew. The interior is divided into forward and rear upper compartments and a single lower deck, total volume of all three compartments being 42,825 cu ft (1,212·7 cu m). The C-5A is intended primarily as a freighter, in which role typical loads may include two M-60 tanks or sixteen 15 cwt lorries; or one M-60, two Iroquois helicopters, five M-113 personnel carriers, one M-59 2½ ton truck and an M-151 5 cwt truck; or ten Pershing missiles with their towing and launching vehicles; or thirty-six standard load pallets. Straight-in cargo loading can be accomplished via the upward-hinged nose and the rear-fuselage ramp/door, simultaneously if necessary. If required as a personnel transport, the C-5A can carry 75 troops on the rear upper deck and 270 on the lower deck.

73 General Dynamics (Convair) B-58 Hustler

Although outweighed in sheer numbers by the larger aeroplane by more than seven to one, the Hustler's purpose was to form, with the Boeing Stratofortress, the front-line retaliation force of the USAF's Strategic Air Command. The Command received its first B-58A in March 1960, somewhat more than three years after the type began flight testing, and the last of the eighty-six production B-58A's built was delivered in October 1962. From these SAC maintained an operations-ready force of about eighty Hustlers, assigned to the 43rd and 305th Bomb Wings based in the USA. The thirty evaluation aircraft included two XB-58 prototypes (first flight 11 November 1956), eleven YB-58A for service test, eight conversions to TB-58A combat trainers and one NB-58A engine testbed. Eleven aircraft were brought up to production B-58A standard in 1961. The Hustler was the world's first supersonic strategic bomber, and established nearly a score of world speed and payload/altitude records. It had an unrefuelled range of some 2,000 miles (3,220 km), and over even longer ranges with the use of in-flight refuelling could maintain average speeds in excess of 1,000 mph (1,610 km/hr). A 3-seater, the Hustler had no internal weapons bay, having been designed as a complete weapons system with an under-fuselage 'mission pod' which formed part of the overall area-ruling of the aircraft in its fully-equipped condition. The lower half of the pod contained fuel, which was used first and then jettisoned; the upper half of the pod contained either bombs, camera packs or ECM equipment. As an alternative to the pod, four small-size nuclear weapons could be carried under the centre of the fuselage. The Hustler's internal equipment included a high degree of automated target location and weapon direction systems; a complete ejection capsule for each member of the crew; and a Vulcan multi-barrel 20 mm cannon for rearward defence. All Hustlers were withdrawn from front-line USAF service in 1970.

INDEX

The reference numbers refer to the illustrations and corresponding text.